A
SECOND COURSE IN
STATISTICS

A SECOND COURSE IN STATISTICS

BY

ROBERT LOVEDAY
M.Sc., F.I.S.

Senior Lecturer in Mathematics and Statistics,
The Technical College,
Kingston-upon-Thames

CAMBRIDGE
AT THE UNIVERSITY PRESS
1961

PUBLISHED BY
THE SYNDICS OF THE CAMBRIDGE UNIVERSITY PRESS

Bentley House, 200 Euston Road, London, N.W. 1
American Branch: 32 East 57th Street, New York 22, N.Y.
West African Office: P.O. Box 33, Ibadan, Nigeria

©

CAMBRIDGE UNIVERSITY PRESS
1961

Printed in Great Britain at the University Press, Cambridge
(Brooke Crutchley, University Printer)

Contents

CONTENTS

vi

CONTENTS

vii

CONTENTS

CONTENTS

Preface

Although this volume is called *A Second Course in Statistics* and although it meets the needs of students who are preparing for Statistics as an Advanced or Scholarship Level subject of the G.C.E., it is not in any way an advanced treatise. It merely completes the school treatment of the subject that was begun in *A First Course in Statistics*. It is primarily a school textbook providing for the sixth-form pupil some interesting applications of pure mathematics.

It may, however, also prove very useful to students in Universities, Training Colleges, Colleges of Technology and Colleges of Agricultural Science who are meeting the subject for the first time. It may indeed form the basis of a first-year course for University Specialists before they proceed to a more rigorous mathematical treatment in their second year.

The keyword of *A First Course in Statistics* is *observation*. The uninitiated student is unable to extract ideas from Statistics until he has learnt the common methods of classifying and representing data. He has to learn *what meaning* can be attached to the terms commonly used in Statistical Analysis. In a first course the idea of significance should be avoided and all differences at this stage should be absolutely blatant.

In *A Second Course in Statistics* the important idea is *probability*. At this stage the student must be able to decide how much *confidence* he can place in his results; whether the small differences he observes are *significant* or not.

The contents of this book form a definite course. The chapters have a logical sequence leading to a short account of Quality Control followed by a treatment of regression lines by the method of least squares and of correlation coefficients. It is not intended, nor is it easy, for the reader to select a chapter from the middle of the book and study it without knowledge of the preceding chapters although chapters 10–12 form an independent section.

R. L.

1 July 1960

Preliminary Revision Exercises

ON THE MEAN AND THE STANDARD DEVIATION

(Students should refer to the glossary for definitions and formulae.)

1. Measurements are made to the nearest inch of the heights of 100 children. Draw the frequency diagram of the following distribution:

Height	60	61	62	63	64	65	66	67	68
Frequency	2	0	15	29	25	12	10	4	3

Calculate the mean, and the standard deviation from the mean.

[London]

2. The following values of a quantity x were obtained experimentally:

x	18	19	20	21	22	23	24	25	26
Frequency	1	5	8	12	10	7	4	1	2

Calculate the mean and the standard deviation and draw the histogram for this distribution.

[London]

3. Find the mean and standard deviation of the set of numbers 8, 9, 10, 11, 12. From this set, ten samples each containing two numbers can be selected. Find the mean of each of these samples and calculate the standard deviation of these means.

[London]

4. Two forms, one of 20 boys and the other of 30 boys, are given an examination. In the smaller form the average mark was 60 and the standard deviation was 7·0. In the other form the average mark was 50 and the standard deviation was 10·0. Find the standard deviation for the marks of the 50 boys taken as a single group.

[London]

5. The numbers of members, means and standard deviations of three distributions are:

No. of members	280	350	630
Means	45	54	49
Standard deviations	6	4	8

Find the mean and standard deviation of the distribution formed by the three distributions taken together.

[London]

6. The mean of the ages of n_1 boys is M_1, and the standard deviation from the mean of their age distribution is σ_1. The mean of the ages of n_2 girls is M_2, and the corresponding standard deviation from the mean is σ_2. Find the mean of the ages of the boys and girls combined.

If $M_1 = M_2$, obtain an expression for the standard deviation from the mean of the combined age distribution.

[London]

7. The marks obtained by ten boys in an examination were 12, 17, 20, 23, 26, 29, 29, 35, 38, 41.

Find the standard deviation. The marks are now to be adjusted so that the mean is 60 and the standard deviation is 15. Calculate the highest and the lowest marks obtained on the new scale. What is the purpose of this adjustment? [London]

8. The table gives the number of minutes late or early for the arrival of a train on a number of runs:

Late	2	4	1	6	9	2	1	0
Early	3	1	.	.	.	.	.	.

Calculate the mean of these and the standard deviation.

After two more runs neither the mean nor the standard deviation is altered. Calculate, to the nearest half, the number of minutes late or early for each of these runs. [London]

9. Four boys sit for an examination. The average of their marks is M and the standard deviation is σ. The marks are converted to a new scale by the formula

$$y = 50 - 20(M-x)/\sigma,$$

where y is the new mark and x is the original mark. Find the mean and the standard deviation of the new marks.

If the original marks were 47, 57, 65, 71, find the new marks each to the nearest integer. [London]

10. The marks obtained by the n candidates who passed an examination but did not reach the credit standard ranged from 68 to 76. They were converted to a range of 50 to 60 by reading off the new mark, y, corresponding to an old mark, x, from the straight line graph joining the point (68, 50) to the point (76, 60). Find a formula for y in terms of x and deduce relationships between (i) the new mean, $\bar{y}$, and the old mean, $\bar{x}$; (ii) the new standard deviation, s', and the old standard deviation, s. [Northern]

11. The numbers 1, 2, 3, 4, 5, 6 are printed one on each of six cards. Three cards are drawn at random and the numbers on each of them are added together. In 100 trials the following distribution is obtained:

Total	6	7	8	9	10	11	12	13	14	15
Frequency	3	6	9	16	15	11	17	12	5	6

Calculate the mean and standard deviation of this distribution. Would you expect the mean to rise or fall if the number of trials were greatly increased, assuming that every selection is equally probable? [London]

12. Two dice, each of which has its faces numbered from 1 to 6, are thrown together, and the score found by squaring the difference between the numbers on the faces resting uppermost. Draw up a table showing the number of ways in which each possible score can be obtained. Determine the mean score and calculate the standard deviation from this mean. [London]

1

The Normal Distribution

1. The normal probability curve. The equation of the normal probability curve in its most convenient form is

$$y = \frac{1}{\sqrt{(2\pi)}}\, e^{-\frac{1}{2}x^2}.$$

It was originally derived by Gauss as the law of the probable distribution of errors of measurement and hence it is often called the *Gaussian* or *error* curve. It is a continuous function for which x may range from $-\infty$ to $+\infty$, but the part of the curve which has real practical value lies between $x = -4$ and $x = +4$. Ordinary books of mathematical tables contain values of e^x and e^{-x} and the student will have no difficulty in using them to obtain values of the ordinate y of the normal probability curve for given values of x. The normal probability curve, however, is of such fundamental importance in statistical analysis that it is useful to have values of y, tabulated for given values of x as in table A1,* page 139.

2. Negative values of x. Since y is a function of x^2, negative values of x such as -1, -2, -3 give the same positive value to y as the positive values 1, 2, 3. Thus the graph of the function is symmetrical about the y-axis.

3. The graph of the function. The graph of

$$y = \frac{1}{\sqrt{(2\pi)}}\, e^{-\frac{1}{2}x^2}$$

between $x = -4$ and $x = +4$ is shown in fig. 1. The student can construct it for himself by using the values given in table A1.

4. The area under the curve. The dotted rectangles shown in fig. 1 are each of unit width and their heights are the ordinates at -3.5, -2.5, -1.5, -0.5, $+0.5$, $+1.5$, $+2.5$ and $+3.5$. Their areas are, therefore,

0·0009, 0·0175, 0·1295, 0·3521, 0·3521, 0·1295, 0·0175, 0·0009.

* Those table numbers preceded by a capital 'A' are to be found in the Appendix.

Thus the area under the graph between $x = -4$ and $x = +4$ is approximately unity. Note that the two rectangles between $x = -4$ and $x = -3$ and between $x = 3$ and 4 are so small that they have been left to the imagination.

Actually the area between $-\infty$ and $+\infty$ can be proved to be exactly unity. Mathematically this is stated as

$$\frac{1}{\sqrt{(2\pi)}} \int_{-\infty}^{\infty} e^{-\frac{1}{2}x^2} \, dx = 1.$$

The above approximation of unity for the area between -4 and $+4$ is a basis for the statement in §1 that the part of the curve which is of real practical value is that between -4 and $+4$.

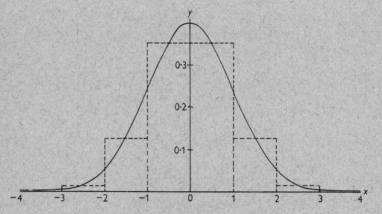

Fig. 1. The normal probability curve. The continuous bell-shaped curve is the graph of

$$y = \frac{1}{\sqrt{(2\pi)}} e^{-\frac{1}{2}x^2}.$$

The dotted rectangles are used to show that the area under the curve is approximately unity. The rectangle between $x = 3$ and $x = 4$ is left to the imagination and similarly that between $x = -4$ and $x = -3$.

5. Exercises using Simpson's rule. Simpson's rule, that an approximation for the area A under $y = f(x)$ between two ordinates y_1 and y_3, at a distance $2h$ apart is

$$A = \tfrac{1}{3}h\{y_1 + 4y_2 + y_3\},$$

where y_2 is the mid-ordinate can be used, in conjunction with table A 1, to obtain approximations for the area under the probability curve between given values of x. Thus, for the area between $x = 0$ and $x = 1$,

$$2h = 1, \quad y_1 = 0 \cdot 3989, \quad y_2 = 0 \cdot 3521, \quad y_3 = 0 \cdot 2420,$$

and an approximation for the area is

$$A = \tfrac{1}{6}\{0\cdot3989 + 1\cdot4084 + 0\cdot2420\}$$
$$= 0\cdot3416.$$

The student will find it a useful exercise to verify, by similar calculations, that

   (i) the area between $x = 1$ and $x = 2$ is approximately $0\cdot1357$,

   (ii) the area between $x = 2$ and $x = 3$ is approximately $0\cdot0214$,

   (iii) the area between $x = 3$ and $x = 4$ is approximately $0\cdot00135$.

6. The area under the graph to the left of a given ordinate. The area under the probability curve is of great practical importance. Table A2, page 140, shows the area $A(x)$ under the graph to the left of a given

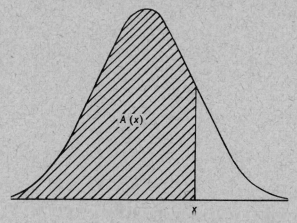

Fig. 2. The area $A(x)$ to the left of a given value of x is tabulated in table A2. Mathematically expressed,

$$A(x) = \frac{1}{\sqrt{(2\pi)}} \int_{-\infty}^{x} e^{-\frac{1}{2}t^2}\, dt.$$

value of x as illustrated in fig. 2. Thus $A(0) = 0\cdot5000$ indicates that half of the area under the graph is to the left of $x = 0$ and $A(1) = 0\cdot8413$ indicates that $0\cdot8413$ of the area (i.e. $84\cdot13\,\%$) is to the left of $x = 1$. Moreover $A(1) - A(0) = 0\cdot3413$ indicates that $0\cdot3413$ of the area (i.e. $34\cdot13\,\%$) is between the ordinates at $x = 0$ and $x = 1$.

7. $A(x)$ for negative value of x. Table A2 indicates that $A(1\cdot96) = 0\cdot975$. Thus $97\cdot5\,\%$ of the area is to the left of $x = 1\cdot96$ and $2\cdot5\,\%$ to the right of $x = 1\cdot96$. As the graph is symmetrical about the y-axis it follows that $2\cdot5\,\%$ of the area lies to the left of $x = -1\cdot96$ and hence

$$A(-1\cdot96) = 1 - A(1\cdot96).$$

In general it may be stated that the area to the left of a negative value of x is obtained by subtracting from unity the area to the left of the corresponding positive value of x. In symbols this is written

$$A(-x) = 1 - A(x).$$

and it is illustrated diagrammatically in fig. 3.

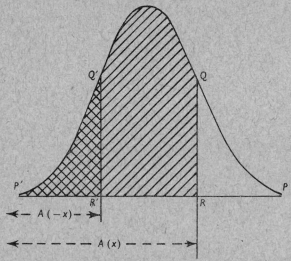

Fig. 3. Illustrates that $A(-x) = 1 - A(x)$ because area PQR = area $P'Q'R'$.

8. The mean and the standard deviation. The normal probability distribution given in tables A1 and A2 has its mean situated at the origin, $x = 0$, and its standard deviation is unity. If the heights of a group of men are known to be normally distributed about a mean of 68 in. with a standard deviation of 2 in. then heights in inches of 68, 68+2, 68+4, 68+6, 68+8 must be regarded as replacing $x = 0, 1, 2, 3, 4$ and $A(1) - A(0) = 0·3413$ indicates that 0·3413 of the total number of men in the group will probably be between 68 and 70 in. in height while $A(2) - A(1) = 0·1359$ indicates that 0·1359 of the total number will probably be between 70 and 72 in. in height and so on.

The examples and exercises in the following paragraphs illustrate various practical applications of the mean and standard deviation of a normal distribution.

9. How to construct a normal frequency distribution when given its mean and its standard deviation. *Jackets for young men are made in the following sizes, according to chest measurement*

Size	1	2	3	4	5	6
Chest measurement (in.)	30–	32–	34–	36–	38–	40–42

The chest measurements of young men in a certain age range are known to be normally distributed with mean 35·63 in. and standard deviation 2·00 in. Estimate the percentages of young men in this age range likely to require each of the six sizes and also the percentages likely to fall above or below the size range. [Northern]

TABLE I A

Chest measurement x (in.)	Deviation of chest measurement from mean $x - \bar{x}$ (in.)	Standardized chest measurement $\dfrac{x - \bar{x}}{\sigma} = X$	Value from table A2 of $A(X)$	$A(X)$ expressed as a percentage $100\,A(X)$
30	−5·63	−2·815	0·00244	0·244
32	−3·63	−1·815	0·0347	3·47
34	−1·63	−0·815	0·2075	20·75
36	+0·37	+0·185	0·5734	57·34
38	+2·37	+1·185	0·8820	88·20
40	+4·37	+2·185	0·98556	98·556
42	+6·37	+3·185	0·99927	99·927

The first step of the calculation is seen in table 1 A. The chest measurements x are set down in column one with their deviations from the mean chest measurement $\bar{x}$ in column two. These deviations are then *standardized* by dividing them by the standard deviation σ. The standardized chest measurements X of the third column are then used to obtain from table A2 the values $A(X)$ of column four. In column five the values $A(X)$ are finally expressed as percentages. The percentage of young men likely to require size 1 is then

$$100A(-1\cdot815) - 100A(-2\cdot815) = 3\cdot23$$

and the percentage likely to require size 2 is

$$100A(-0\cdot815) - 100A(-1\cdot815) = 17\cdot28.$$

By continuing this process the percentages of young men likely to require each of the six sizes can be obtained and set out as shown in table 1 B. Also, the percentage likely to fall below the size range is

$$100A(-2\cdot815) = 0\cdot244,$$

while the percentage likely to fall above the size range is

$$100 - 100A(3\cdot185) = 0\cdot073.$$

These figures are also included in table 1 B.

10. The histogram. Table 1 B can be illustrated diagrammatically as the *histogram* shown in fig. 4. Note that, although the distribution is normal, the histogram is not symmetrical because the size divisions are not symmetrical about the mean.

TABLE 1B

Chest measurement (in.)	Below 30	30–	32–	34–	36–	38–	40–42	Above 42
Size	—	1	2	3	4	5	6	—
Percentage of young men requiring the size	0·24	3·23	17·28	36·59	30·86	10·37	1·37	0·07

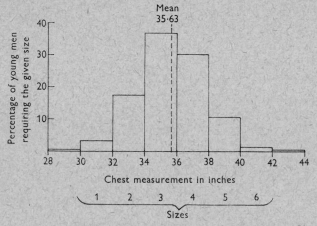

Fig. 4. Histogram showing the distribution in sizes of jackets for young men.

11. Exercises.

1. A sugar refiner uses a machine which packs automatically 1 lb. cartons of sugar. When the machine is in operation the cartons emerge from it in a continuous stream ready for sale. In order to check that the machine is giving correct weight sample cartons are taken at random from it and weighed accurately. From these random samples it is estimated that the mean weight of carton delivered by the machine is 16·4 oz. and that the standard deviation of the weights of the cartons is 0·16 oz. Assuming that the weights are normally distributed construct a frequency table showing the percentage of cartons the machine delivers (i) less than 15·8 oz., (ii) between 15·8 oz. and 16·0 oz., (iii) between 16·0 and 16·2 oz., (iv) between 16·2 oz. and 16·4 oz., (v) between 16·4 oz. and 16·6 oz., (vi) between 16·6 oz. and 16·8 oz., (vii) between 16·8 oz. and 17·0 oz., (viii) over 17·0 oz.

Illustrate diagrammatically by drawing a histogram.

2. The mean *length of life* of a certain type of television tube is 1600 hr. with a standard deviation of 250 hr. Assuming that the lengths of life of television tubes of this type are normally distributed, copy, and complete, the following frequency table and use it to draw a histogram:

Length of life (hr.)	Less than 750	750– 1000	1000– 1250	1250– 1500	1500– 1750	1750– 2000	2000– 2250	More than 2250
Percentage of tubes								

3. The *recovery time* of an aircraft is the time between landing and being ready to fly again. In an investigation on a certain type of aircraft it was found that the recovery times were normally distributed about a mean of 19 min. with a standard deviation of 3 min. Make out a frequency table showing the percentage of aircraft with recovery times 5 min. to 10 min., 10 min. to 15 min., 15 min. to 20 min., etc., and draw the histogram.

4. An investigation into the weekly spending money of the 400 boys in a certain school showed that the mean was 6s. 10d. and the standard deviation 11d. Assuming that the distribution was normal, calculate the theoretical frequencies for the intervals 4s. to 5s., 5s. to 6s., ..., 9s. to 10s. Draw the histogram. [Northern]

12. An example in which it is assumed that the variability of production can be controlled. *The heights in inches of 'one inch' compression springs produced in a workshop are normally distributed about a mean length of 1·005 in. with standard deviation 0·003 in. Estimate the limits which will contain the central 50 % of production.*

If the mean remains unchanged, find the value to which the standard deviation must be reduced in order that these limits should contain 90 % of production.

The central 50 % of the normal probability curve lies between the values x_1 and x_2 where $A(x_1) = 0.25$ and $A(x_2) = 0.75$. Table A2 shows that $A(x_2) = 0.75$ when $x_2 = 0.675$. Thus $x_2 = 0.675$ and $x_1 = -0.675$ and the central 50 % of production lies between

$$(\text{mean} - 0.675\sigma) \quad \text{and} \quad (\text{mean} + 0.675\sigma),$$

where σ is the standard deviation.

The required range is, therefore,

$$(1.005 - 0.675 \times 0.003) \quad \text{to} \quad (1.005 + 0.675 \times 0.003),$$

i.e. 1·003 in. to 1·007 in. (to the nearest thousandth of an inch).

The central 90 % of the normal probability curve lies between the values x_1 and x_2 where $A(x_1) = 0.05$ and $A(x_2) = 0.95$. Table A2 shows that $A(x_2) = 0.95$ when $x_2 = 1.645$. Thus $x_2 = 1.645$ and $x_1 = -1.645$ and the central 90 % of production lies between

$$(\text{mean} - 1.645\sigma_1) \quad \text{and} \quad (\text{mean} + 1.645\sigma_1),$$

where σ_1 is the new standard deviation.

If these limits are the same as the previous limits

$$1.645\sigma_1 = 0.675\sigma$$

and
$$\sigma_1 = \frac{0.675\sigma}{1.645}$$

$$= 0.00123 \text{ in.}$$

9

A final summary of this example is as follows: *While the standard deviation remains at* 0·003 *in. only* 50 % *of the production lies between* 1·003 *in. and* 1·007 *in. but if the standard deviation can be reduced to* 0·001 *in. the variability of production will have been controlled to such an extent that more than* 90 % *of the production will lie between these limits.*

13. An example in which the mean is adjusted, the variability remaining constant. *Estimate the percentage of underweight packets which the machine described in* §11, *Ex.* 1, *is delivering.*

The Board of Trade will allow machines of this kind to deliver up to 5 % *of their packets underweight. If the machine is to comply with this regulation calculate the lowest value to which the mean may legally be lowered and estimate the amount of sugar that would thus be saved in* 2240 *packets.*

The specified weight of 16 oz. is 0·4 oz. *below* the mean and the standard deviation is 0·16 oz. The standardized value of 16 oz. is, therefore, $-0·4/0·16 = -2·5$.

Now
$$A(-2·5) = 1 - A(2·5)$$
$$= 1 - 0·99379$$
$$= 0·00621.$$

Hence about 0·6 % of the packets are underweight.

If 5 % of the packets are to be underweight $A(x) = 0·05$ gives the standardized value x of 16 oz. *with respect to the new mean.*

Therefore
$$A(-x) = 0·95$$
$$-x = 1·645$$
$$x = -1·645.$$

This indicates that 16 oz. is $1·645 \times 0·16$ oz. *below* the new mean and hence the new mean is 16·3 oz. correct to one decimal place. When the machine is delivering packets of mean weight 16·4 oz., the amount of sugar given away as overweight in 2240 packets is

$$(0·4 \times 2240/16) \text{ lb.} = 56 \text{ lb.}$$

When the mean weight is reduced to 16·3 oz. the amount given away is $(0·3 \times 2240/16)$ lb. $= 42$ lb. The adjustment of the mean thus effects a saving of 14 lb. of sugar in 2240 packets.

14. Exercises.

1. Tests on electric lamps of a certain type indicated that their lengths of life were normally distributed about a mean of 1860 hr. with a standard deviation of 68 hr. Estimate the percentage of lamps which can be expected to burn (i) more than 2000 hr., (ii) less than 1750 hr.

2. Steel rods which are being manufactured to a specification of 1·5 in. diameter are acceptable if they are within the *tolerance limits* 1·505 in. and 1·495 in. If the diameters are normally distributed about a mean 1·501 in. with standard deviation 0·003 in., estimate the percentage of rods that will be rejected (i) oversize, (ii) undersize.

3. Limit gauges are used to reject all components in which a certain dimension is greater than 3·02 in. or less than 2·98 in. It is found that about 5 % are rejected oversize and 5 % are rejected undersize. Assuming that the dimensions are normally distributed, find the mean and standard deviation of the distribution.

Estimate what the percentages of rejects would be if the limits were (i) 3·015 in. to 2·985 in., (ii) 3·025 in. to 2·975 in.

4. A machine makes electrical resistors having a mean resistance of 100 ohms with a standard deviation of 5 ohms. It is observed that a certain firm rejects approximately 11 % of the resistors (5½ % over and 5½ % under) because they are not within its *tolerance limits*. Assuming the distribution of values to be normal, estimate what tolerance limits are employed by the firm.

5. In trials of the effectiveness of detergents in washing-up the measure x of performance is the number of plates which can be washed before the foam on the water is reduced to a thin surface layer. For a certain detergent x is known to be approximately normally distributed with mean 25 and standard deviation 4. Draw the frequency curve for this distribution, taking a scale of 1 in. to 4 plates and making the area equal to 5 sq. in.

In fifty trials of a new detergent x has the frequency distribution given below:

x	21–24	25–28	29–32	33–36	37–40
Frequency	1	4	37	6	2

On the same diagram as before draw a histogram of area 5 sq. in. to represent these data. Describe in words the changes in performance resulting from the use of the new detergent. [Northern]

6. The weights of loaves of bread made in a large bakery are normally distributed with standard deviation 0·25 oz., and the mean of the distribution is so placed that only 0·1 % of the loaves produced have weights falling below the statutory minimum of 28 oz. The weekly output of loaves averages 250,000 and the cost in pence of producing a loaf of weight w oz. is given by the formula $3 + 0·11w$. If by the installation of new dough-dividing machinery the standard deviation could be reduced to 0·10 oz., and the mean allowed to fall just far enough to give the same percentage below the statutory minimum as before, determine the average saving in pounds sterling per week. [Northern]

2

Probability

15. Casting a die. When an ordinary die is cast, each of the numbers *one, two, three, four, five, six* has an *equal chance* of falling uppermost. There is, therefore, 1 *chance out of* 6 of obtaining a *six* and we say that

$$\text{the probability of throwing a six} = \tfrac{1}{6}.$$

16. Playing cards. An ordinary pack of 52 playing cards contains 4 *aces* and hence, if we select at random 1 card from a well-shuffled pack, there are 4 chances out of 52 of it being an *ace*. Thus

$$\text{the probability of selecting an ace} = \tfrac{4}{52} = \tfrac{1}{13}.$$

Further,

$$\text{the probability of selecting the ace of spades} = \tfrac{1}{52}.$$

17. Tossing a coin. When a coin is tossed it may fall either as a *head* or a *tail* and thus

$$\text{the probability of a head} = \tfrac{1}{2}.$$

18. Definition of probability. Sections 15, 16 and 17 are simple illustrations of the definition of probability which is as follows: *When all the equally possible occurrences have been enumerated the probability of a particular event is the ratio of the number of ways in which the particular event may occur to the total number of possible occurrences.*

19. The meaning of probability. When we say that the probability of throwing a *six* is $\tfrac{1}{6}$ we do not mean that exactly 1 throw out of every 6 will produce a *six*. If the student actually throws a die 60 times it is *likely* that he will obtain approximately 10 *sixes*. If he throws one 600 times a *reasonable estimate* of the number of *sixes* he can expect is 100 but it is very unlikely that it will be exactly 100. The following table gives the results of an actual experiment in which a die was cast 648 times. The frequency of each number approximates to 108 which is what we should expect since the probability of each number is $\tfrac{1}{6}$:

Number thrown	1	2	3	4	5	6
Frequency	96	98	117	130	107	100

20. Success and failure. If we regard the throwing of a *six* as a *success* and the throwing of any other number as a *failure*, the probability of

12

success is $\frac{1}{6}$ and the probability of failure is $\frac{5}{6}$. It is customary to use the letter p for the probability of success and the letter q for the probability of failure. Thus $p = \frac{1}{6}$ and $q = \frac{5}{6}$ and $q = 1-p$.

In §16, if the selecting of an *ace* is a success, $p = \frac{1}{13}$ and $q = \frac{12}{13}$ while in §17, if a *head* is a success, $p = \frac{1}{2}$ and $q = \frac{1}{2}$ also.

21. Total probability. Suppose a boy casts a die and that he is to receive a prize if he obtains a *six* OR a *one*. The probability of him winning a prize is

$$\tfrac{1}{6}+\tfrac{1}{6} = \tfrac{1}{3}.$$

This example illustrates the *theorem of total probability* which states: *The probability that ONE OR OTHER of several MUTUALLY EXCLUSIVE events shall occur is the SUM of the probabilities of the separate events.* Note particularly that the throwing of a *six* excludes the possibility of a *one* and the throwing of a *one* excludes the possibility of a *six*.

22. Compound probability. Suppose the boy casts a die, selects a card from a well-shuffled pack and tosses a coin and that he is to receive a prize only if he obtains a *six* AND an *ace* AND a *head*. The probability of his success is then

$$\tfrac{1}{6} \times \tfrac{1}{13} \times \tfrac{1}{2} = \tfrac{1}{156}.$$

This is an example of the *theorem of compound probability* which states: *If the probabilities of several independent events are $p_1, p_2, ..., p_n$, the probability that ALL will take place is the PRODUCT $p_1 p_2 ... p_n$.*

23. The use of $q = 1-p$. Suppose the boy of §22 is to receive a prize provided

    (i) he throws a *six* but neither selects an *ace* nor tosses a *head,*
OR (ii) he selects an *ace* but neither throws a *six* nor tosses a *head,*
OR (iii) he tosses a *head* but neither throws a *six* nor selects an *ace.*

Consider case (i). The probability that he throws a *six* is $\frac{1}{6}$, the probability that he does not select an *ace* is $1-\frac{1}{13} = \frac{12}{13}$ and the probability that he does not toss a *head* is $\frac{1}{2}$. Thus the probability of case (i) occurring is $\frac{1}{6} \times \frac{12}{13} \times \frac{1}{2}$. Similarly the probabilities of cases (ii) and (iii) are $\frac{1}{13} \times \frac{5}{6} \times \frac{1}{2}$ and $\frac{1}{2} \times \frac{5}{6} \times \frac{12}{13}$ respectively and (i), (ii) and (iii) are mutually exclusive events. Hence the total probability of the boy's success is

$$\tfrac{1}{6} \times \tfrac{12}{13} \times \tfrac{1}{2} + \tfrac{1}{13} \times \tfrac{5}{6} \times \tfrac{1}{2} + \tfrac{1}{2} \times \tfrac{5}{6} \times \tfrac{12}{13} = \tfrac{77}{156}.$$

This example illustrates the use of the important principle: *If the probabilities of several independent events are $p_1, p_2, p_3, ..., p_n$, the probability that the first takes place and that the others do not is*

$$p_1(1-p_2)(1-p_3)...(1-p_n).$$

13

24. Examples.

1. *If three dice are thrown together, what is the probability of obtaining*

(i) 3 *fives*;

(ii) 1, *and only* 1, *five*;

(iii) *at least* 1 *five?*

(i) By the theorem of compound probability, the probability of 3 *fives* is $(\frac{1}{6})^3 = \frac{1}{216}$.

(ii) By the method of §23, the first die may be a *five* with the second and third not *or* the second a *five* and the first and third not *or* the third a *five* with the first and second not. Thus the total probability is $3(\frac{1}{6} \times \frac{5}{6} \times \frac{5}{6}) = \frac{25}{72}$.

(iii) The probability of obtaining at least 1 *five*

$$= 1 - \text{the probability of obtaining no } \textit{fives}$$

$$= 1 - (\tfrac{5}{6})^3$$

$$= \tfrac{91}{216}.$$

2. *If two cards are drawn from a well-shuffled pack of 52 playing cards, what is the probability that*

(i) *they are both aces*;

(ii) *neither of them is an ace*;

(iii) *at least one of them is an ace?*

(i) The probability that the first is an ace is $\frac{4}{52}$.

If the first is an ace there are only 3 aces left in the remaining 51 cards and the probability that the second is an ace is $\frac{3}{51}$. Thus the probability that both are aces is $(\frac{4}{52}) \times (\frac{3}{51}) = \frac{1}{221}$.

(ii) The probability that neither of them is an ace is $(\frac{48}{52}) \times (\frac{47}{51}) = \frac{188}{221}$.

(iii) The probability that at least one of them is an ace is

$$1 - (\tfrac{188}{221}) = \tfrac{33}{221}.$$

3. *A box contains ten radio valves all apparently sound, although four of them are actually substandard. Find the chance that, if two of the valves are taken from the box, they are both substandard.*   [Northern]

The probability that the first taken from the box is substandard is $\frac{4}{10}$. If the first taken from the box is substandard, the probability that the second is also substandard is $\frac{3}{9}$. Hence the probability that both are substandard is $\frac{4}{10} \times \frac{3}{9} = \frac{2}{15}$. An alternative reasoning for this result is given in §29.

4. *In a cricket match each over consists of six balls and the bowling is opened by two players A and B, the player A bowling the first over. If the probability that A takes a wicket with each ball is $\frac{1}{12}$ and the corresponding probability for B is $\frac{1}{15}$, show that the probability that A takes at least one wicket in his first over is approximately $\frac{2}{5}$ whilst the probability that he takes a wicket before B is approximately $\frac{2}{3}$.* [Northern]

The probability that A does not take a wicket in his first over is $(\frac{11}{12})^6 = 0.5932$. Hence the probability that he takes at least one wicket in his first over is $1 - 0.5932 = 0.4068$ which is approximately $\frac{2}{5}$.

We have just proved that the probability that A takes his first wicket in his first over is 0.4068. The probability that neither B nor A take wickets in their first overs but that A takes his first wicket in his second over is $(\frac{11}{12})^6(\frac{14}{15})^6 \times 0.4068$. The probability that neither B nor A take wickets in their first two overs but that A takes his first wicket in his third over is $(\frac{11}{12})^{12}(\frac{14}{15})^{12} \times 0.4068$, and so on. Thus the infinite geometric progression

$$0.4068 + (\tfrac{11}{12})^6(\tfrac{14}{15})^6 \times 0.4068 + (\tfrac{11}{12})^{12}(\tfrac{14}{15})^{12} \times 0.4068 + \ldots$$

gives the total probability that A will take a wicket before B. The sum to infinity of this geometric progression is

$$\frac{0.4068}{1 - (\frac{11}{12})^6(\frac{14}{15})^6} = \frac{0.4068}{0.6081}$$

which is approximately $\frac{2}{3}$.

5. *Three per cent of the sparking-plugs manufactured by a firm are defective. Calculate the probability of getting at least one defective plug in a random sample of four.*

Because 3 % are defective we can assume that the probability of any plug selected at random being defective is 0.03 and the probability of it being sound is 0.97. Thus the probability of a random sample of four being all sound is $(0.97)^4 = 0.8855$ and the probability of at least one being defective is $1 - 0.8855 = 0.1145$ which is approximately $\frac{1}{9}$.

25. Exercises.

1. When three marksmen take part in a shooting contest their chances of hitting the target are $\frac{1}{2}$, $\frac{1}{3}$ and $\frac{1}{4}$. Calculate the chance that one, and only one, bullet will hit the target if all three men fire at it simultaneously. [Northern]

2. The independent probabilities that three components of a television set will need replacing within a year are $\frac{1}{10}$, $\frac{1}{12}$ and $\frac{1}{15}$. Calculate the probability that (i) at least one component, (ii) one and only one component, will need replacing. [Northern]

3. Five per cent of a large consignment of eggs are bad. Find the probability of getting at least one bad egg in a random sample of a dozen.

[Northern]

4. A bag contains 7 black balls and 3 white balls. If they are drawn one by one from the bag, find the probability of drawing first a black, then a white and so on alternately until only black balls remain.

5. Three of five dice are each numbered in the normal way, but the fourth is numbered 1, 2, 3, 6, 5, 6 and the fifth 1, 6, 3, 6, 5, 6. If the five dice are thrown together, calculate the probability of turning up (i) five 6's, (ii) at least four 6's, (iii) at least one 6.

[Northern]

6. Four players A, B, C, D in this order throw a die in turn. Find for each player the probability of his being first to throw a six. Explain how the sum of the four probabilities forms a useful check.

[Northern]

3

Random Selection

26. The symbol $\binom{n}{r}$ or ^nC_r. The symbol $\binom{n}{r}$ or ^nC_r denotes the number of ways of *choosing* (or *selecting*) r things from n unlike things. It is alternatively stated to be the number of *combinations* (or *selections*) of n unlike things taken r at a time and it is proved in textbooks of Algebra that

$$\binom{n}{r} = \frac{n(n-1)(n-2)\ldots(n-r+1)}{1.2.3\ldots r}.$$

Thus, the number of ways of choosing a sample of 4 radio valves from a box of 10 is

$$\binom{10}{4} = \frac{10.9.8.7}{1.2.3.4}$$
$$= 210$$

and if the 4 valves are *chosen at random* each of these 210 ways are equally probable.

Again, the number of ways of choosing 3 cards from an ordinary pack of 52 playing cards is

$$\binom{52}{3} = \frac{52.51.50}{1.2.3}$$
$$= 22100.$$

27. The factorial notation $n!$ or $\underline{|n}$. The symbol $n!$ or $\underline{|n}$ is used to denote the product of the first n positive integers. Thus

$$n! = 1.2.3\ldots n.$$

For example

$$7! = 1.2.3.4.5.6.7 = 5040,$$

and

$$4! = 1.2.3.4. = 24.$$

An alternative method of writing

$$\binom{10}{4} = \frac{10.9.8.7}{1.2.3.4}$$

is, therefore,

$$\binom{10}{4} = \frac{10.9.8.7}{1.2.3.4} \times \frac{6.5.4.3.2.1}{1.2.3.4.5.6}$$
$$= \frac{10!}{4!\,6!}$$

and in general it is customary to write

$$\binom{n}{r} = \frac{n!}{r!\,(n-r)!}.$$

28. Selecting and rejecting. The number of ways of selecting 11 players from the 14 members of a cricketing party is

$$\binom{14}{11} = \frac{14.13.12.11.10.9.8.7.6.5.4}{1.2.3.4.5.6.7.8.9.10.11}$$

$$= 364.$$

Clearly, this is more conveniently calculated by using the fact that the number of ways of selecting the 11 players from the 14 members is the same as the number of ways of selecting the 3 non-players which is

$$\binom{14}{3} = \frac{14.13.12}{1.2.3}$$

$$= 364.$$

Thus
$$\binom{14}{11} = \binom{14}{3}$$

and in general
$$\binom{n}{r} = \binom{n}{n-r}.$$

The last equation is stated in words as follows: *The number of ways of selecting r things from n unlike things is the same as the number of ways of rejecting (n−r).*

29. The use of $\binom{n}{r}$ in examples on probability. In §24, Ex. 2, it was shown that if 2 cards are selected at random from a well-shuffled pack of 52 playing cards, the probability that they are both aces is $\frac{1}{221}$ whilst the probability that neither are aces is $\frac{188}{221}$. An alternative argument which leads to these same values is as follows:

(i) The probability that both are aces

$$= \frac{\text{the number of ways of selecting 2 aces from the 4 in the pack}}{\text{the number of ways of selecting any 2 of the 52 cards in the pack}}$$

$$= \binom{4}{2}\Big/\binom{52}{2}$$

$$= \frac{4.3}{1.2}\Big/\frac{52.51}{1.2}$$

$$= \frac{1}{221}.$$

(ii) The probability that neither are aces

$$= \frac{\text{the number of ways of selecting 2 cards from the 48 which are not aces}}{\text{the number of ways of selecting any 2 of the 52 cards}}$$

$$= \binom{48}{2} \Big/ \binom{52}{2}$$

$$= \frac{48.47}{1.2} \Big/ \frac{52.51}{1.2}$$

$$= \tfrac{188}{221}.$$

The result of §24, Ex. 3, might be established by a similar argument as follows:

The probability that both valves are substandard is

$$= \frac{\text{the number of ways of choosing any 2 of the 4 substandard valves}}{\text{the number of ways of choosing any 2 of the 10 valves}}$$

$$= \binom{4}{2} \Big/ \binom{10}{2}$$

$$= \frac{4.3}{1.2} \Big/ \frac{10.9}{1.2}$$

$$= \tfrac{2}{15}.$$

30. Experiments with playing cards.

Experiment 1. *Suppose we draw at random 5 cards from a well-shuffled pack and note the number of spades.*

(i) The probability that *none* are spades is

$$\binom{39}{5} \Big/ \binom{52}{5} = 0.2215.$$

(ii) The probability that 1 is a spade and 4 are not is calculated as follows:

The number of ways of selecting 4 which are not spades is $\binom{39}{4}$.

The number of ways of selecting 1 which is a spade is $\binom{13}{1}$.

Each selection of 4 which are not spades can be combined with each selection of 1 which is a spade to form a different choice of 5 cards and hence

$$\binom{39}{4} \times \binom{13}{1}$$

is the complete number of ways of selecting 5 cards, 4 of which are not spades and 1 of which is a spade.

Thus, the probability that 1 is a spade and 4 are not is

$$\binom{39}{4} \times \binom{13}{1} \Big/ \binom{52}{5} = 0.4114.$$

Table 3A summarizes all possible cases. To test the theory experimentally the student should take a pack of cards and

(i) shuffle it thoroughly,
(ii) draw out 5 cards at random,
(iii) note how many of the 5 are spades,
(iv) replace the 5 cards.

If this cycle of four operations is repeated 50 times, the observed frequencies thus obtained should approximate quite closely to the probable frequencies of table 3A obtained by multiplying the probabilities by 50.

TABLE 3A

Number of spades in the random sample of 5	Probability	Probable frequency for 50 random samples
0	$\binom{39}{5} \Big/ \binom{52}{5} = 0.2215$	11
1	$\binom{39}{4} \binom{13}{1} \Big/ \binom{52}{5} = 0.4114$	20
2	$\binom{39}{3} \binom{13}{2} \Big/ \binom{52}{5} = 0.2743$	14
3	$\binom{39}{2} \binom{13}{3} \Big/ \binom{52}{5} = 0.0816$	4
4	$\binom{39}{1} \binom{13}{4} \Big/ \binom{52}{5} = 0.0107$	1
5	$\binom{13}{5} \Big/ \binom{52}{5} = 0.0005$	0

Experiment 2. Suppose we draw at random 5 cards from a well-shuffled pack and note the number of aces. Similar arguments to those of Experiment 1 enable us to establish table 3B which should again be tested experimentally.

31. The number of ways of selecting like things. It will be realised that the probabilities shown in table 3A apply equally well to a random sample of 5 balls drawn from a bag containing 13 black balls and

39 balls of other colours, or to a random sample of 5 cycle lamp batteries taken from a box containing 52 batteries 13 of which are defective. In this connection it is important to note that the number of ways of selecting 5 black balls from 13 which are all alike is $\binom{13}{5}$ = 1287 even though it is impossible to tell the difference between these 1287 selections. Thus, although only one selection is apparent, there are 1287 ways of making it. Probabilities are calculated from the number of ways in which selections can be made. The examples which follow should help to make clear the distinction between 'the number of selections' and 'the number of ways of selecting'.

TABLE 3B

Number of aces in the random sample of 5	Probability	Probable frequency for 50 random samples
0	$\binom{48}{5} \Big/ \binom{52}{5} = 0 \cdot 6589$	33
1	$\binom{48}{4} \binom{4}{1} \Big/ \binom{52}{5} = 0 \cdot 2995$	15
2	$\binom{48}{3} \binom{4}{2} \Big/ \binom{52}{5} = 0 \cdot 0399$	2
3	$\binom{48}{2} \binom{4}{3} \Big/ \binom{52}{5} = 0 \cdot 0017$	0
4	$\binom{48}{1} \binom{4}{4} \Big/ \binom{52}{5} = 0 \cdot 0000 \, (2)$	0

32. Examples.

1. (i) If 3 letters are chosen from the word SWEETER how many selections are possible?

(ii) What is the probability that a random selection of 3 letters from the same word contains at least 2 E's?

(i) If 3 E's are chosen, only 1 selection is possible.

If 2 E's and 1 other letter are chosen, 4 selections are possible.

If 1 E and 2 other letters are chosen, $\binom{4}{2}$ = 6 selections are possible.

If no E's and 3 other letters are chosen, $\binom{4}{3}$ = 4 selections are possible.

Hence the total number of selections is 15.

(ii) The probability that the selection contains 3 E's

$$= \frac{\text{the no. of ways of selecting 3 E's}}{\text{the no. of ways of selecting 3 letters from 7}}$$

$$= 1 \Big/ \binom{7}{3}$$

$$= \tfrac{1}{35}.$$

The probability that the selection contains 2 E's

$$= \frac{\text{the no. of ways of combining 2 E's from 3 with 1 other letter from 4}}{\text{the no. of ways of selecting 3 letters from 7}}$$

$$= \frac{\binom{3}{2} \times \binom{4}{1}}{\binom{7}{3}}$$

$$= \tfrac{12}{35}.$$

Hence the probability that a random selection of 3 letters contains at least 2 E's is $\tfrac{13}{35}$.

2. Three balls are drawn at random from a bag containing 3 red, 4 white and 5 black balls. Calculate the probabilities that the 3 balls are (i) all black, (ii) 1 red, 1 white, 1 black.   [Northern]

(i) The probability that the 3 balls are all black

$$= \frac{\text{the no. of ways of selecting 3 balls from 5 black}}{\text{the no. of ways of selecting 3 balls from 12}}$$

$$= \binom{5}{3} \Big/ \binom{12}{3}$$

$$= \tfrac{1}{22}.$$

(ii) The probability that 1 is red, 1 is black and 1 is white

$$= \binom{3}{1}\binom{4}{1}\binom{5}{1} \Big/ \binom{12}{3}$$

$$= \tfrac{3}{11}.$$

3. A department in a works has 10 machines which may need adjustment from time to time during the day. Three of these machines are old, each having a probability of $\tfrac{1}{11}$ of needing adjustment during the day, and 7 are new, having corresponding probabilities of $\tfrac{1}{21}$.

Assuming that no machine needs adjustment twice on the same day, determine the probabilities that on a particular day

(i) just 2 old and no new machines need adjustment,

(ii) if just 2 machines need adjustment, they are of the same type.

[Northern]

(i) The probability that 2 of the old machines need adjustment but that the third does not, is $(\frac{1}{11})^2(\frac{10}{11})$.

The 2 old machines which need adjustment can be selected, however, in $\binom{3}{2}$ ways.

Thus the *total* probability that just two of the 3 old machines need adjustment is

$$\binom{3}{2}\left(\frac{1}{11}\right)^2\left(\frac{10}{11}\right).$$

Further, the probability that no new machines need adjustment is $(\frac{20}{21})^7$.

Hence, the *compound* probability that just 2 old and no new machines need adjustment is

$$\binom{3}{2}\left(\frac{1}{11}\right)^2\left(\frac{10}{11}\right)\left(\frac{20}{21}\right)^7 = 0.0160.$$

The student might find the following argument easier.

Let the old machines be X, Y, Z and the new machines A, B, C, D, E, F, G.

The probability that X, Y need adjustment and Z, A, B, C, D, E, F, G do not is $(\frac{1}{11})(\frac{1}{11})(\frac{10}{11})(\frac{20}{21})^7$.

Similarly X, Z may need adjustment but not Y, A, B, C, D, E, F, G, and also Y, Z may need adjustment but not X, A, B, C, D, E, F, G.

Thus the total probability, as before, is $3(\frac{1}{11})^2(\frac{10}{11})(\frac{20}{21})^7$.

(ii) The probability that just 2 new machines and no old machines need adjustment is, similarly,

$$\binom{7}{2}\left(\frac{1}{21}\right)^2\left(\frac{20}{21}\right)^5\left(\frac{10}{11}\right)^3 = 0.0280.$$

'The probability that if just 2 machines need adjustment, they are of the same type' is the same as 'the probability that *either* just 2 old and no new *or* just 2 new and no old need adjustment'. Thus the required probability is

$$0.0160 + 0.0280 = 0.0440.$$

33. Exercises.

1. Each of two bags contains 8 coins. How many different combinations of 6 coins can be made by drawing 3 coins out of each bag, (i) when no

two of the 16 coins are alike, (ii) when two of the coins in one bag are alike?

In case (i) what is the probability that a specified coin will appear in any one combination? [London]

2. In question 1, case (ii) above, what is the probability that at least one of the two like coins will appear in any one combination?

3. A box contains red and green sweets mixed together in the ratio 3 to 2. A handful of 20 sweets is taken at random from the box. Find

(i) the probability that there will be precisely 15 red sweets in the handful,

(ii) the probability that the handful of sweets is such that it can be shared equally between 5 children so that each child receives the same number of red sweets, this number being at least 2. [Northern]

4. In an agricultural experiment barley is to be grown on 8 plots of land arranged in a line, with original fertility measurements as shown in fig. 5:

Plot no.	1	2	3	4	5	6	7	8
Fertility	10	10	11	11	11	11	10	10

Fig. 5

A manurial treatment is applied to 4 of the plots chosen at random. Find the probability that it is applied to precisely 3 plots having a fertility measurement of 11 and one plot having a fertility measurement of 10. Calculate the mean original fertility of manured plots minus the mean original fertility of unmanured plots in this case.

By considering other cases too find the probability distribution of the mean original fertility of manured plots minus the mean original fertility of unmanured plots. [Northern]

5. State the addition and multiplication laws of probability.

A number is chosen at random from each of the two sets

0, 1, 2, 3, 4, 5, 6, 7, 8, 9;
0, 1, 2, 3, 4, 5, 6, 7, 8, 9.

Calculate the probability that

(i) both numbers are odd;

(ii) their sum is not greater than 5. [Northern]

6. A stack of 20 cards contains 4 cards of each of 5 different colours, namely white, black, green, red and blue. Apart from colour the cards are indistinguishable. A set of 3 cards is drawn at random from the stack. Find the chances that the 3 cards are (i) all white, (ii) all of one colour, (iii) all of different colours. [Cambridge]

4

The Binomial Distribution

34. Throwing six dice. Suppose 6 dice are thrown together.

(i) The probability, $P(0)$, that *no* sixes fall uppermost is $(\frac{5}{6})^6$.

(ii) The probability, $P(1)$, that *any one* of the dice has its six uppermost but the *other five* have not, is calculated as follows:

The probability that 5 of the dice are not sixes but that the other is a six is $(\frac{5}{6})^5(\frac{1}{6})$. There are, however, $\binom{6}{1}$ ways of selecting the die which is a six and each of these $\binom{6}{1}$ ways are equally probable. Thus the total probability that any 1 is a six and the other 5 are not is

$$\binom{6}{1}\left(\frac{5}{6}\right)^5\left(\frac{1}{6}\right).$$

(iii) Similarly, the probability, $P(2)$, that *any two* of the dice have their sixes uppermost and the *other four* have not is

$$\binom{6}{2}\left(\frac{5}{6}\right)^4\left(\frac{1}{6}\right)^2.$$

Table 4A summarises all possible cases. It shows also the probable frequencies if the six dice are thrown together 216 times.

The following distribution was obtained in an actual experiment:

No. of sixes	0	1	2	3	4	5	6	Total
Frequency	77	84	34	19	2	0	0	216

The student will notice that the *observed frequencies* of the experiment approximate quite closely to the *expected frequencies* forecast in table 4A. He will find it interesting to obtain his own set of observed frequencies by carrying out the experiment himself.

35. The binomial expansion of $(q+p)^n$. The probabilities in table 4A are the terms of the binomial expansion

$$(q+p)^6 = q^6 + \binom{6}{1}q^5p + \binom{6}{2}q^4p^2 + \binom{6}{3}q^3p^3 + \binom{6}{4}q^2p^4 + \binom{6}{5}qp^5 + p^6,$$

25

where $q = \frac{5}{6}$ and $p = \frac{1}{6}$. It will now be realised that

THE TERMS OF THE GENERAL BINOMIAL EXPANSION

$$(q+p)^n = q^n + \binom{n}{1}q^{n-1}p + \binom{n}{2}q^{n-2}p^2 + \ldots + p^n,$$

WHERE $q = \frac{5}{6}$ AND $p = \frac{1}{6}$ GIVE THE PROBABILITIES OF OBTAINING $0, 1, 2, \ldots, n$ SIXES WHEN n DICE ARE THROWN TOGETHER.

TABLE 4A

No. of sixes x	Probability $P(x)$	Probable frequency for 216 throws $216 . P(x)$
0	$P(0) = \left(\frac{5}{6}\right)^6$	72·34
1	$P(1) = \binom{6}{1}\left(\frac{5}{6}\right)^5\left(\frac{1}{6}\right)$	86·81
2	$P(2) = \binom{6}{2}\left(\frac{5}{6}\right)^4\left(\frac{1}{6}\right)^2$	43·40
3	$P(3) = \binom{6}{3}\left(\frac{5}{6}\right)^3\left(\frac{1}{6}\right)^3$	11·57
4	$P(4) = \binom{6}{4}\left(\frac{5}{6}\right)^2\left(\frac{1}{6}\right)^4$	1·74
5	$P(5) = \binom{6}{5}\left(\frac{5}{6}\right)\left(\frac{1}{6}\right)^5$	0·14
6	$P(6) = \left(\frac{1}{6}\right)^6$	0·00
Total	1	216·00

36. Exercises.

1. Use the binomial expansion of $(q+p)^3$ to calculate the probabilities of obtaining 0, 1, 2, 3 *ones* (or *aces*) when 3 dice are thrown together. Estimate the frequencies that can be expected if the 3 dice are thrown together 216 times and display your results in a table similar to 4A. Test by experiment.

2. Calculate the probabilities of obtaining 0, 1, 2, 3, 4, 5 *threes* when 5 dice are thrown together. Estimate the frequencies that can be expected if the 5 dice are thrown together 100 times and test by experiment.

37. Tossing five coins.
The argument of §33 can easily be modified to show that the terms of the binomial expansion

$$(q+p)^5 = q^5 + \binom{5}{1}q^4p + \binom{5}{2}q^3p^2 + \binom{5}{3}q^2p^3 + \binom{5}{4}qp^4 + p^5,$$

where $q = \frac{1}{2}$ and $p = \frac{1}{2}$, give the probabilities of obtaining 0, 1, 2, 3, 4, 5 *heads* when 5 coins are tossed together. These probabilities together with the expected frequencies for a total of 832 tosses and the observed frequencies of an actual experiment are displayed in table 4B. The student will find it interesting to carry out the experiment himself but not necessarily for such a large number of tosses.

TABLE 4B

No. of heads x	Probability $P(x)$	Expected frequency for 832 tosses $832 . P(x)$	Observed frequency of an actual experiment
0	$P(0) = \left(\frac{1}{2}\right)^5$	26	25
1	$P(1) = \binom{5}{1} \left(\frac{1}{2}\right)^4 \left(\frac{1}{2}\right)$	130	123
2	$P(2) = \binom{5}{2} \left(\frac{1}{2}\right)^3 \left(\frac{1}{2}\right)^2$	260	246
3	$P(3) = \binom{5}{3} \left(\frac{1}{2}\right)^2 \left(\frac{1}{2}\right)^3$	260	264
4	$P(4) = \binom{5}{4} \left(\frac{1}{2}\right) \left(\frac{1}{2}\right)^4$	130	146
5	$P(5) = \left(\frac{1}{2}\right)$	26	28
Total	1	832	832

38. Exercise.

Calculate the probabilities of obtaining 0, 1, 2, 3, 4 *heads* when 4 coins are tossed together. Estimate the frequencies that can be expected if the 4 coins are tossed together 40 times and test by experiment.

39. The sampling-bottle.

The *sampling-bottle* shown in fig. 6 contains a large number of small steel balls 5 % of which are painted black. If one ball is taken at random from the bottle the probability, p, that it is black is $\frac{1}{20}$ or 0·05 and the probability, q, that it is not black is $\frac{19}{20}$ or 0·95. Suppose a random sample of 10 balls is taken from the bottle. The probabilities that the sample contains 0, 1, 2, etc. black balls is given by the terms of the binomial expansion

$$(q+p)^{10} = q^{10} + \binom{10}{1} q^9 p + \binom{10}{2} q^8 p^2 + \text{etc.},$$

where $q = 0.95$ and $p = 0.05$. These probabilities are shown in table 4c. The separate probabilities of 3, 4, 5, etc., black balls appearing in any random sample are so small that they have been combined as *the probability of 3 or more*, $P(x \geqslant 3)$, where

$$P(x \geqslant 3) = 1 - \{P(0) + P(1) + P(2)\}.$$

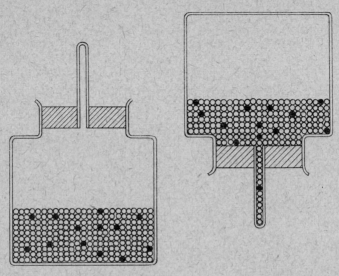

Fig. 6. A sampling-bottle. *Upright position*: the bottle contains a large number of small steel balls 5 % of which are painted black; a hollow glass tube sealed at the outer end and open at the inner end passes through the cork. *Inverted position*: after being well shaken the bottle is turned over and some of the steel balls fall into the hollow glass tube, which is just long enough to allow 10 balls to be visible below the cork.

It will be appreciated that the hollow glass tube passing through the cork is a very convenient arrangement for drawing random samples from the bottle. The process of shaking the bottle, turning it over, counting the number of black balls visible below the cork, is so quick that it can be repeated a hundred times in a few minutes.

40. Exercises.

1. Draw up a table similar to 4c for a sampling-bottle if 10 % of the balls contained in it are black and the glass tube is just long enough to draw random samples of five.

2. Draw up a table similar to 4c for a sampling-bottle if $2\frac{1}{2}$ % of the balls contained in it are black and the glass tube is long enough to draw samples of twenty.

TABLE 4C

No. of black balls in the random sample of 10 x	Probability $P(x)$	Expected frequency for 100 samples $100.P(x)$
0	$P(0) = (0.95)^{10} = 0.598$	59.8
1	$P(1) = \binom{10}{1}(0.95)^9(0.05) = 0.315$	31.5
2	$P(2) = \binom{10}{2}(0.95)^8(0.05)^2 = 0.075$	7.5
3 or more	$P(x \geqslant 3) = 1 - \{P(0)+P(1)+P(2)\} = 0.012$	1.2
Total	1	100.0

41. Sampling in industry. The experiments carried out with the sampling-bottle lead directly to the method of sampling as it is applied in the testing of mass-produced articles which are either accepted or rejected according as to whether or not they satisfy specification requirements. If, for example, 5 % of the screws manufactured by a certain process are rejected because they fail to satisfy tolerance requirements, table 4C gives the probabilities of a random sample of 10 screws containing 0, 1, 2, 3 or more rejects. Also, if 100 samples are inspected the frequencies for 0, 1, 2, 3 or more rejects per sample should approximate fairly closely to the expected frequencies of table 4C, any large divergence signifying that the proportion of rejects in the bulk differs significantly from 5 %. The examples and exercises which follow will serve to make clear the important practical applications of the binomial distribution.

42. Examples.

1. (i) *In a large lot of electric-light bulbs 5 % of the bulbs are defective. Calculate the probability that a random sample of 20 will contain at most 2 defective bulbs.*

(ii) *One third of the lots presented for inspection have 5 % defective, the rest 10 % defective. If a lot is rejected when a random sample of 20 taken from it contains more than 2 defective bulbs, find the proportion of lots which are rejected.* [Northern]

(i) Using the terms of the binomal expansion

$$(q+p)^{20} = q^{20} + \binom{20}{1}q^{19}p + \binom{20}{2}q^{18}p^2 + \dots$$

29

with $p = 0.05$ and $q = 0.95$ it is convenient to tabulate the calculation in a form similar to table 4C, as shown in table 4D.

Thus, the probability that a random sample of 20 will contain at most 2 defective bulbs is 0.9236. This means that for lots which have 5 % defective about 92 % of the samples will have at most 2 defective bulbs and 8 % of the samples will have more than 2 defective bulbs.

TABLE 4D

No. of defective bulbs in random sample of 20 x	Probability $P(x)$
0	$P(0) = (0.95)^{20} = 0.3581$
1	$P(1) = \binom{20}{1}(0.95)^{19}(0.05) = 0.3770$
2	$P(2) = \binom{20}{2}(0.95)^{18}(0.05)^2 = 0.1885$
At most 2	$P(x \leqslant 2) = P(0)+P(1)+P(2) = 0.9236$

TABLE 4E

No. of defective bulbs in random sample of 20 x	Probability $P(x)$
0	$P(0) = (0.9)^{20} = 0.1213$
1	$P(1) = \binom{20}{1}(0.9)^{19}(0.1) = 0.2696$
2	$P(2) = \binom{20}{2}(0.9)^{18}(0.1)^2 = 0.2846$
At most 2	$P(x \leqslant 2) = P(0)+P(1)+P(2) = 0.6755$

(ii) Table 4E gives values for lots which have 10 % defective $p = 0.1$ and $q = 0.9$.

Thus, for lots which have 10 % defective about 68 % of the samples will have at most 2 defective bulbs and 32 % of the samples will have more than 2 defective bulbs.

Let us suppose that 300 lots are presented for inspection, 100 of them having 5 % defective and 200 having 10 % defective. Then 8 of the 100 and 2×32 of the 200 will be rejected.

Thus 72 of the 300 lots will be rejected.

This means that 24 % of all the lots presented for inspection will be rejected.

2. *Assuming that the probability that any one of 8 telephone lines is engaged at an instant is $\frac{1}{4}$, calculate the probability that*

(i) *at least one of the lines is engaged,*

(ii) *all 8 lines are engaged.*

What is the most probable number of lines engaged at any instant and what is the probability that this number of lines is engaged?

The simplest method of calculation is by a table similar to 4c (table 4F).

TABLE 4F

No. of lines engaged x	Probability $P(x)$
0	$P(0) = (\frac{3}{4})^8 = 0\cdot1002$
1	$P(1) = \binom{8}{1} \left(\frac{3}{4}\right)^7 \left(\frac{1}{4}\right) = 0\cdot2669$
2	$P(2) = \binom{8}{2} \left(\frac{3}{4}\right)^6 \left(\frac{1}{4}\right)^2 = 0\cdot3114$
3	$P(3) = \binom{8}{3} \left(\frac{3}{4}\right)^5 \left(\frac{1}{4}\right)^3 = 0\cdot2076$
⋮	⋮
8	$P(8) = (\frac{1}{4})^8 = 0\cdot00001524$

The probability that at least one line is engaged is
$$P(1)+P(2)+P(3)+\ldots+P(8) = 1-P(0)$$
$$= 0\cdot8998,$$
which is approximately $\frac{9}{10}$.

The probability that all the lines are engaged is $0\cdot00001524$. The most probable number of lines engaged at any instant is 2 and the probability of this number of lines being engaged is $0\cdot3114$ (rather less than $\frac{1}{3}$).

A more direct method of obtaining the last two answers is as follows: The probabilities $P(0)$, $P(1)$, $P(2)$, etc. continue to increase provided
$$\frac{P(x+1)}{P(x)} \geqslant 1.$$

Now

$$\frac{P(x+1)}{P(x)} = \frac{\binom{8}{x+1}\left(\frac{3}{4}\right)^{7-x}\left(\frac{1}{4}\right)^{x+1}}{\binom{8}{x}\left(\frac{3}{4}\right)^{8-x}\left(\frac{1}{4}\right)^{x}}$$

$$= \left\{\frac{8!}{(x+1)!\,(7-x)!} \Big/ \frac{8!}{x!\,(8-x)!}\right\}\frac{\left(\frac{1}{4}\right)}{\left(\frac{3}{4}\right)}$$

$$= \frac{(8-x)}{3(x+1)}.$$

Thus $\dfrac{P(x+1)}{P(x)} \geqslant 1$ provided $(8-x) \geqslant 3(x+1)$.

This gives $x \leqslant \frac{5}{4}$ and hence $P(2)$ is the greatest probability.

43. Exercises.

1. In the manufacture of screws by a certain process it was found that 8 % of the screws were rejected because they failed to satisfy tolerance requirements. What was the probability that a sample of 10 screws contained (i) exactly 2, (ii) not more than 2 rejects?

2. Fifty samples of 20 are drawn from a large bulk in which the proportion of defective items is 12 %. Calculate the number of samples that can be expected to include 0, 1, 2, etc. defectives.

3. If on the average rain falls on 12 days in every 30 find the probability (i) that the first 3 days of a given week will be fine and the remainder wet; (ii) that rain will fall on just 3 days of a given week.   [London]

4. A marksman's chance of hitting a target with each of his shots is $\frac{3}{5}$. If he fires 6 shots calculate his chance of (i) exactly 3 hits, (ii) at least 3 hits.

5. In a cricket match the probability that a certain bowler takes a wicket with any ball is $\frac{1}{15}$. Calculate the probability of him taking (i) 3 wickets in 3 balls, (ii) at least 1 wicket in 6 balls.

6. The probability that a tennis player will serve an 'ace' is $\frac{1}{4}$. What is the probability that she will serve exactly 4 aces out of 7 services?

44. Verification that the mean of the binomial distribution is np.

(i) From table 4A, the mean number of sixes per throw,

$$\bar{x} = \tfrac{1}{216}\{72\cdot34 \times 0 + 86\cdot81 \times 1 + 43\cdot40 \times 2 + 11\cdot57 \times 3 + 1\cdot74 \times 4 + 0\cdot14 \times 5\}$$

$$= 1.$$

(ii) From table 4B, the mean number of heads per toss,

$$\bar{x} = \tfrac{1}{832}\{26 \times 0 + 130 \times 1 + 260 \times 2 + 260 \times 3 + 130 \times 4 + 26 \times 5\}$$

$$= 2\tfrac{1}{2}.$$

(iii) From table 4c it is only possible to obtain an approximate value for the mean number of black balls per sample because of the combined probability for '3 or more'. This approximate value

$$\bar{x} = \tfrac{1}{100}\{59 \cdot 8 \times 0 + 31 \cdot 5 \times 1 + 7 \cdot 5 \times 2 + 1 \cdot 2 \times 3\}$$

$$= 0 \cdot 501.$$

The above three values (i), (ii) and (iii) of $\bar{x}$ are examples of the following valuable property of the binomial distribution which will be proved formally in §45.

If a variate x takes the values $0, 1, 2, \ldots, n$ with probabilities equal respectively to the terms, arranged in the usual way, of the binomial expansion of $(q+p)^n$, where $q+p = 1$, then the mean value of x is np.

Thus   (i) in table 4A, $n = 6$, $p = \tfrac{1}{6}$ and the mean $np = 1$,

          (ii) in table 4B, $n = 5$, $p = \tfrac{1}{2}$ and the mean $np = 2\tfrac{1}{2}$,

and   (iii) in table 4C, $n = 10$, $p = 0 \cdot 05$ and the mean $np = 0 \cdot 5$.

45. The mean and variance of the binomial distribution. By setting down the binomial distribution as shown in table 4G its mean and variance can easily be deduced. In theoretical work of this kind the probabilities of column (ii) are often called *relative frequencies*.

TABLE 4G

(i) Variate x	(ii) Probability or relative frequency f	(iii) fx (i) × (ii)	(iv) fx^2 (i) × (iii)
0	q^n	0	0
1	$nq^{n-1}p$	$nq^{n-1}p$	$nq^{n-1}p$
2	$\dfrac{n(n-1)}{1.2}q^{n-2}p^2$	$\dfrac{n(n-1)}{1}q^{n-2}p^2$	$\dfrac{2n(n-1)}{1}q^{n-2}p^2$
3	$\dfrac{n(n-1)(n-2)}{1.2.3}q^{n-3}p^3$	$\dfrac{n(n-1)(n-2)}{1.2}q^{n-3}p^3$	$\dfrac{3n(n-1)(n-2)}{1.2}q^{n-3}p^3$
$\vdots$	$\vdots$	$\vdots$	$\vdots$
n	p^n	np^n	n^2p^2
Total	Σf	Σfx	Σfx^2

Now $\Sigma f = 1$,

$$\Sigma fx = np\left\{q^{n-1} + \frac{(n-1)}{1}q^{n-2}p + \frac{(n-1)(n-2)}{1.2}q^{n-3}p^2 + \ldots + p^{n-1}\right\}$$

$$= np(q+p)^{n-1}$$

$$= np,$$

and $\Sigma fx^2 = np\left\{q^{n-1}+\dfrac{2(n-1)}{1}q^{n-2}p+\dfrac{3(n-1)(n-2)}{1.2}q^{n-3}p^2+\ldots+np^{n-1}\right\}$

$\quad = np\left\{q^{n-1}+\dfrac{(n-1)}{1}q^{n-2}p+\dfrac{(n-1)(n-2)}{1.2}q^{n-3}p^2+\ldots+p^{n-1}\right.$

$\qquad\quad \left.+\dfrac{(n-1)}{1}q^{n-2}p+\dfrac{2(n-1)(n-2)}{1.2}q^{n-3}p^2+\ldots+(n-1)p^{n-1}\right\}$

$\quad = np\{(q+p)^{n-1}+(n-1)p(q+p)^{n-2}\}$

$\quad = np\{1+(n-1)p\}$

$\quad = np(1-p)+(np)^2.$

Thus the mean, $\qquad\qquad\dfrac{\Sigma fx}{\Sigma f} = np$

and the variance, $\qquad\dfrac{\Sigma fx^2}{\Sigma f}-\left(\dfrac{\Sigma fx}{\Sigma f}\right)^2 = npq.$

46. How to estimate the proportion of black balls in a sampling-bottle.

Let us now suppose that the proportion of black balls in a sampling-bottle is unknown and that 100 samples of 8 drawn from the bottle give the following distribution:

No. of black balls in the sample of 8 $\quad x$	0	1	2	3	4	5 or more	Total
No. of samples	32	41	20	6	1	0	100

The mean number of black balls per sample

$$\bar{x} = \tfrac{1}{100}\{32\times0+41\times1+20\times2+6\times3+1\times4\}$$
$$= 1\cdot03,$$

and in this case $n = 8$.

Hence $\bar{x} = np$ gives $1\cdot03 = 8p$ and thus

$$p = 0\cdot13 \text{ approximately.}$$

This means that 13 % of the balls in the bottle are black. Here then is a valuable method of estimating the proportion p of defective items in a bulk by examining random samples of n items.

47. Estimation of the proportion of defective items in a bulk.

The items produced by a certain machine were checked by examining samples of 12. The following table shows the distribution of 50 samples according to the number of defective items they contained:

No. of defectives in a sample of 12	0	1	2	3	4	5 or more	Total
No. of samples	18	19	9	3	1	0	50

Calculate the mean number of defectives per sample and, assuming that the binomial law applies, estimate the proportion of defective items in the whole bulk produced by the machine.

By an easy calculation the mean number of defectives per sample is 1, and since $n = 12$, it follows that $p = \frac{1}{12}$.

Thus $100p = 8\frac{1}{3}\%$ is the estimated proportion of defective items in the whole bulk.

48. Exercises.

1. Razor blades of a certain kind are sold in packets of five. The following table shows the frequency distribution of 100 packets according to the number of faulty blades contained in them:

No. of faulty blades	0	1	2	3	4	5
No. of packets	80	17	2	1	0	0

Calculate the mean number of faulty blades per packet and, assuming that the binomial law applies, estimate the probability that a blade taken at random from any packet will be faulty. [Northern]

2. The production of an electrical component is checked by examining samples of 6. The following table shows the frequency distribution of 40 samples according to the number of defective components contained in each:

No. of defective components in sample of 6	0	1	2	3	4	5 or 6
No. of samples	12	16	8	3	1	0

Estimate the proportion of defective components in the whole output.

3-2

5

The Poisson Distribution

49. Introductory. Consider the four sampling-bottles shown in fig. 7. Bottle A contains a large number of steel balls of which 10 % are black and random samples of 5 are drawn from it. The probabilities $P(0)$, $P(1)$, $P(2)$, $P(x \geqslant 3)$ of 0, 1, 2, 3 *or more* black balls per sample are calculated, as shown in §39, by the binomial expansion of $(q+p)^n$ where $p = \frac{1}{10}$, $q = \frac{9}{10}$ and $n = 5$. Bottle B contains a large number of steel balls of which 5 % are black and random samples of 10 are drawn from it. Thus, for bottle B, $p = \frac{1}{20}$, $q = \frac{19}{20}$ and $n = 10$. Similarly, for bottle C, $p = \frac{1}{40}$, $q = \frac{39}{40}$ and $n = 20$ while for bottle D, $p = \frac{1}{100}$, $q = \frac{99}{100}$ and $n = 50$. In bottles A, B, C and D, therefore, p decreases and n increases in such a way that if a large number of samples are drawn from any bottle the mean number of black balls per sample, np, will be the same for all four bottles. Table 5A gives the probabilities $P(0), P(1), P(2), P(x \geqslant 3)$ for each of the four bottles.

TABLE 5A
The binomial distribution of probabilities

No. of black balls per sample x	Bottle A $p = \frac{1}{10}$ $n = 5$ $P(x)$	Bottle B $p = \frac{1}{20}$ $n = 10$ $P(x)$	Bottle C $p = \frac{1}{40}$ $n = 20$ $P(x)$	Bottle D $p = \frac{1}{100}$ $n = 50$ $P(x)$
0	$P(0) = 0{\cdot}590$	$P(0) = 0{\cdot}598$	$P(0) = 0{\cdot}603$	$P(0) = 0{\cdot}603$
1	$P(1) = 0{\cdot}328$	$P(1) = 0{\cdot}315$	$P(1) = 0{\cdot}309$	$P(1) = 0{\cdot}304$
2	$P(2) = 0{\cdot}073$	$P(2) = 0{\cdot}075$	$P(2) = 0{\cdot}075$	$P(2) = 0{\cdot}075$
3 or more	$P(x \geqslant 3) = 0{\cdot}009$	$P(x \geqslant 3) = 0{\cdot}012$	$P(x \geqslant 3) = 0{\cdot}013$	$P(x \geqslant 3) = 0{\cdot}018$

When p is small and n is large as in the case of bottle D it is more convenient to calculate $P(0), P(1), P(2), \ldots$, from the terms of

$$e^{-a} \times \{\text{expansion of } e^a\}$$

$$= e^{-a}\left\{1 + a + \frac{a^2}{2!} + \ldots\right\}$$

$$= e^{-a} + ae^{-a} + \frac{a^2}{2!}e^{-a} + \ldots,$$

where a is the mean number of black balls per sample.

36

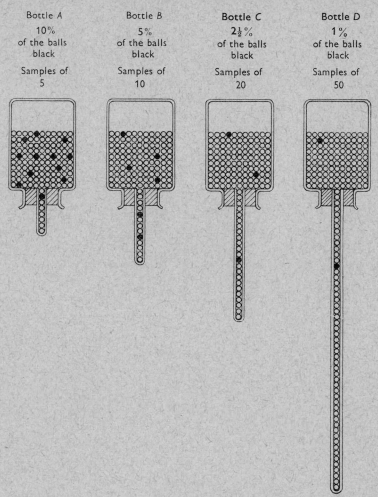

Fig. 7. Four sampling-bottles in which the proportion, p, of black balls decreases while the number, n, in a sample increases so that the mean number of black balls per sample, np, remains constant.

Thus a replaces np and in the example under consideration $a = \frac{1}{2}$.

The probabilities
$$e^{-a},\ ae^{-a},\ \frac{a^2}{2!}e^{-a},\ \frac{a^3}{3!}e^{-a},\ \dots$$

are known as the Poisson distribution. Their formal derivation from the binomial distribution is given in §50. They have been used to calculate the probabilities of table 5B which, it will be seen, approximate very closely indeed to the probabilities for bottle D in table 5A and quite closely to the probabilities for bottles A, B, and C.

37

TABLE 5B

The Poisson distribution of probabilities

$$e^{-a}, \; ae^{-a}, \; \frac{a^2}{2!}e^{-a}, \; ..., \; \text{where } a = \tfrac{1}{2}$$

No. of black balls per sample x	Probability $P(x)$
0	$P(0) = e^{-\frac{1}{2}} = 0.607$
1	$P(1) = \tfrac{1}{2}e^{-\frac{1}{2}} = 0.303$
2	$P(2) = \dfrac{(\frac{1}{2})^2}{2!}e^{-\frac{1}{2}} = 0.076$
3 or more	$P(x \geqslant 3) = 1 - \{P(0)+P(1)+P(2)\} = 0.014$

50. Exercise.

One per cent of the articles produced in a certain workshop are defective. Calculate the probabilities $P(0)$, $P(1)$, $P(2)$, $P(3)$, $P(4)$, $P(x \geqslant 5)$ of 0, 1, 2, 3, 4, 5 or more defective articles in a random sample of 200,

   (i) by substituting $p = 0.01$, $q = 0.99$ and $n = 200$ in the binomial distribution,

   (ii) by substituting $a = 2$ in the Poisson distribution.

(Make use of the values of e^{-a} given on page 145.)

51. The derivation of the Poisson distribution.

In the formal consideration of the binomial and Poisson distributions it is usual to call p the probability of *success* and q ($= 1-p$) the probability of *failure*. The Poisson distribution is the form assumed by the binomial distribution when p is small and n is large, the mean number of successes np being a finite constant a.

In $(q+p)^n$ let $p = a/n$. The probabilities of $0, 1, 2, 3, ...$ successes

$$q^n, \; nq^{n-1}p, \; \frac{n(n-1)}{2!}q^{n-2}p^2, \; \frac{n(n-1)(n-2)}{3!}q^{n-3}p^3, \; ...$$

then become

$$q^n, \; aq^{n-1}, \; \frac{1(1-1/n)}{2!}a^2q^{n-2}, \; \frac{1(1-1/n)(1-2/n)}{3!}a^3q^{n-3}, \; ....$$

When n is large, p is small, q is approximately unity and the terms of the distribution are proportional to

$$1, \; a, \; \frac{a^2}{2!}, \; \frac{a^3}{3!}, \; ...,$$

whose sum is e^a. The sum of the actual probabilities, however, is unity since it is the limit of $(p+q)^n$. The actual probabilities are therefore

38

obtained by dividing each of the above terms by their sum e^a. Thus the probabilities of $0, 1, 2, 3, \ldots$ successes are

$$e^{-a}, \; ae^{-a}, \; \frac{a^2}{2!}e^{-a}, \; \frac{a^3}{3!}e^{-a}, \; \ldots$$

respectively.

52. The mean and variance of the Poisson distribution. By setting down the Poisson distribution as shown in table 5c its mean and variance can easily be deduced.

TABLE 5C

(i) No. of successes x	(ii) Probability or relative frequency f	(iii) fx (i) × (ii)	(iv) fx^2 (i) × (iii)
0	e^{-a}	0	0
1	ae^{-a}	ae^{-a}	ae^{-a}
2	$\dfrac{a^2}{1.2}e^{-a}$	$\dfrac{a^2}{1}e^{-a}$	$\dfrac{2a^2}{1}e^{-a}$
3	$\dfrac{a^3}{1.2.3}e^{-a}$	$\dfrac{a^3}{1.2}e^{-a}$	$\dfrac{3a^3}{1.2}e^{-a}$
⋮	⋮	⋮	⋮
Total	Σf	Σfx	Σfx^2

Now
$$\Sigma f = 1,$$

$$\Sigma fx = ae^{-a}\left\{1 + \frac{a}{1} + \frac{a^2}{1.2} + \ldots\right\}$$

$$= ae^{-a}e^a$$

$$= a,$$

and
$$\Sigma fx^2 = ae^{-a}\left\{1 + \frac{2a}{1} + \frac{3a^2}{1.2} + \ldots\right\}$$

$$= ae^{-a}\left\{\left(1 + \frac{a}{1} + \frac{a^2}{1.2} + \ldots\right) + \left(\frac{a}{1} + \frac{2a^2}{1.2} + \ldots\right)\right\}$$

$$= ae^{-a}\{e^a + ae^a\}$$

$$= a + a^2.$$

Hence the mean,
$$\frac{\Sigma fx}{\Sigma f} = a$$

and the variance,
$$\frac{\Sigma fx^2}{\Sigma f} - \left(\frac{\Sigma fx}{\Sigma f}\right)^2 = a.$$

The variance of a Poisson distribution is, therefore, equal to the mean of the distribution.

53. An example in which p is small and n is large. *Before a consignment of potatoes may be exported as seed potatoes a random sample of* 300 *has to be inspected and found free of infection. Show that if the average rate of infection in the consignment is* 1 %, *then there is approximately a* 95 % *chance that it will not be passed.*　　　　　　　　　　[Cambridge]

The mean rate of infection for a sample of 300 is 3 and substituting $a = 3$ in the Poisson formula we find that the probability of a sample being free from infection is

$$e^{-3} = 0 \cdot 0498$$
$$= 5 \% \text{ approximately.}$$

Hence the probability that the consignment will not be passed is approximately 95 %.

54. A traffic example. Let us imagine an open stretch of country road. We can assume that the vehicles pass freely along it, quite independent of each other and at completely random times. If 300 vehicles pass a certain point on the road in 2 hr. the average traffic rate is $2\frac{1}{2}$ vehicles per minute and the probabilities $P(0), P(1), P(2), \dots$ of $0, 1, 2, \dots$ vehicles passing the point in any minute can be obtained by substituting $a = 2\frac{1}{2}$ in the Poisson formula (see table 5D).

TABLE 5D

No. of vehicles in any minute x	Probability $P(x)$
0	$P(0) = e^{-2\cdot5} = 0\cdot082$
1	$P(1) = 2\cdot5e^{-2\cdot5} = 0\cdot205$
2	$P(2) = \dfrac{2\cdot5^2}{2!}e^{-2\cdot5} = 0\cdot256$
3	$P(3) = \dfrac{2\cdot5^3}{3!}e^{-2\cdot5} = 0\cdot213$
4 or more	$P(x \geqslant 4) = 1 - \{P(0)+P(1)+P(2)+P(3)\} = 0\cdot244$

55. Exercises.

1. Certain mass-produced articles, of which 0·5 % are defective, are packed in cartons each containing 100. What proportion of cartons are free from defective articles and what proportion contain 2 or more defectives?
　　　　　　　　　　　　　　　　　　　　　　　　　[R.S.S.]

2. Assuming that breakdowns in a certain electric power supply occur according to the Poissonian law with an average of one breakdown in 10 weeks calculate the probabilities of 0, 1, 2 or more breakdowns in any period of one week.

3. If the average number of calls made on a certain telephone route is 20 per hour calculate the probabilities of 0, 1, 2, 3, 4 or more calls being made in any period of 3 min.

4. When 3 dice are cast, the probability of obtaining 3 aces is $\frac{1}{216}$. If the 3 dice are cast 108 times and a prize is awarded every time 3 aces are obtained, calculate the probabilities of 0, 1, 2 or more prizes being awarded.

5. In a large consignment of eggs the average number broken in a crate is 3. Estimate the probability of a crate containing (i) no broken eggs, (ii) more than 3 broken eggs.

6. Assuming that railway accidents occur with relative frequencies that conform to the Poissonian law and that there is on the average 1 accident in 2 years, estimate the probability of 2 accidents occurring within a period of 3 months.

7. If, on the average each year 1 miner out of every 2000 loses his life in a colliery accident, use the Poisson distribution to estimate what chance a colliery which employs 800 miners has of being free of fatal accidents in any given year.

8. Show that for a Poisson distribution the variance equals the mean, and use this result to test the following distribution for conformity to the Poisson law:

No. of defects per piece of cloth	0	1	2	3	4	5	Total
Frequency of pieces	15	26	21	19	8	3	92

[R.S.S.]

9. Compute the average m and standard deviation σ of the following distribution and verify that approximately $\sigma = \sqrt{m}$.

x	0	1	2	3	4	5	Total
f	20,983	2,615	183	14	2	3	23,800

Assuming that the frequencies are given by the formula $Nm^r e^{-m}/r!$ where $N = 23,800$ and r takes successive values 0, 1, 2, 3, 4, 5, compute the expected frequencies from this formula taking m equal to the computed average.

[R.S.S.]

10. Derive the Poisson distribution

$$Ne^{-m}\left(1+m+\frac{m^2}{1.2}+\dots\right)$$

as a limiting form of the binomial distribution $N(p+q)^n$. Find the mean and standard deviation for the table of deaths of women over 85 years old recorded in *The Times* in a three-year period.

No. of deaths recorded on the day	0	1	2	3	4	5	6	7
No. of days	364	376	218	89	33	13	2	1

Find the expected number of days with 'one death recorded' for the Poisson series fitted to the data. [R.S.S.]

11. A car-hire firm has 2 cars, which it hires out by the day. The number of demands for a car on each day is distributed as a Poisson distribution, with mean 1·5.

Calculate the proportion of days on which neither of the cars is used, and the proportion of days on which some demand is refused.

If each car is used an equal amount, on what proportion of days is a given one of the cars not in use? What proportion of demands has to be refused?

[R.S.S.]

6

The χ^2-Distribution

56. The null hypothesis. In many examples and exercises so far, we have *assumed* without question that a distribution is normal, binomial or Poisson. By means of the χ^2-distribution (pronounced *kye-squared* and often printed *chi-squared*) shown in table A4, page 143, it is possible to estimate the extent to which such an *assumption* or *null hypothesis* is justified. The χ^2-distribution has other uses, illustrations of which will be given in this and the next chapter. Its mathematical derivation, however, is completely beyond the scope of this volume.

57. The use of χ^2 for testing normality. The distribution of the weights of the men who rowed in the first and second divisions of the Cambridge University Lent Bumping Races in 1956 is shown in table 6A (the weights of the coxes have been excluded). A cursory inspection of the distribution, or its histogram, reveals that it is roughly normal. Thus, if we regard it as a sample of Cambridge rowing men in general, we are led to expect that the weights of the latter are normally distributed. To decide more definitely whether the distribution of weights is normal or not the first step is to use the mean, 168·8 lb., and the standard deviation 14·44 lb. to construct a normal distribution with the same class intervals, as shown in table 6B. (Sheppard's correction was used to obtain the value 14·44.) The frequencies of table 6A are called the

TABLE 6A
Observed frequencies
Weights of crews in the first and second divisions of the Cambridge University Lent Bumping Races, 1956 (weights of coxes excluded)

Weight (lb.)	130–	140–	150–	160–	170–	180–	190–	200–	210–	220 and over
Frequency	2	22	48	65	72	29	11	5	0	2

TABLE 6B
Expected frequencies
Normal distribution of weights having the same mean, standard deviation and total as the weights of table 6A

Weight (lb.)	Less than 140	140–	150–	160–	170–	180–	190–	200–	210 and over
Frequency	5	20	45	66	64	38	14	3	1

observed frequencies and those of table 6B the *expected* frequencies. The former are the definite *observations* of a statistical investigation. The latter are to be *expected* if the *assumption* or *null hypothesis* that the distribution is normal is true. The question now arises: *Are the differences between the observed and expected frequencies great enough to force us to reject the null hypothesis as false or are they small enough to allow us to accept it as true?* In statistics we generally put this question as: *Are the differences SIGNIFICANT or not?*

58. The calculation of χ^2. To answer the question of the last paragraph it is necessary to calculate χ^2 by the formula

$$\chi^2 = \Sigma \left[\frac{(O-E)^2}{E} \right],$$

where O is the observed frequency of a particular class and E is the corresponding expected frequency.

TABLE 6C
Calculation of χ^2

Weight (lb.)	Observed frequency O	Expected frequency E	$O-E$	$\dfrac{(O-E)^2}{E}$ to 2 decimals
Less than 150	24	25	-1	0·04
150–	48	45	$+3$	0·20
160–	65	66	-1	0·02
170–	72	64	$+8$	1·00
180–	29	38	-9	2·13
190 and over	18	18	0	0·00
Total	256	256	0	$3·39 = \chi^2$

The actual calculation is shown in table 6C. One important point needs some explanation. The mathematical derivation of the χ^2-distribution requires that all the observed and expected frequencies shall be *sufficiently large*. 'Sufficiently large' in this case is usually taken to mean *a minimum of* 10 but in industrial applications the frequency in a class is often allowed to fall as low as 5. A minimum of 10 should be taken as the standard, but where convenience requires it, the standard may be lowered a little. Bearing this in mind the classes at the beginning and end of tables 6A and 6B have been combined before entering them into table 6C.

59. The number of degrees of freedom, ν. Having calculated $\chi^2 = 3·39$ we need to note the *number of degrees of freedom, ν* (pronounced *new*) that were available in its calculation. The conception of 'degrees of freedom' is not an easy one. It will not be fully discussed here but the method of calculating v in each of the examples which follow will be carefully described and this should enable the student to develop a working knowledge of it. In table 6c there are 6 pairs of O and E values or 6 *classes*. The *number of restrictions* imposed in calculating the expected frequencies were 3 in that the expected frequencies have the same *total*, *mean* and *standard deviation* as the observed frequencies. The number of degrees of freedom

$v =$ the number of classes − the number of restrictions

$= 6$ classes − 3 restrictions

$= 3$.

Table A3, page 142, summarises the rules by which the student can obtain v when testing the common types of distributions and contingency tables.

60. The acceptance or rejection of the null hypothesis. Table A4, page 143, gives the percentage points, P, of the χ^2-distribution for different values of v. The column of values for $P = 5$ are of special importance and a few of these values are reprinted for convenience in table 6D.

TABLE 6D

The P = 5 % values of the χ^2-distribution

v	χ^2
1	3·84
2	5·99
3	7·81
4	9·49
5	11·07

If χ^2 is greater than the $P = 5\%$ value, the differences between the observed and expected frequencies are usually taken to be so significant that the null hypothesis must be rejected.

The value of χ^2, 3·39, for $v = 3$ is certainly not greater than the $P = 5\%$ value, 7·81. We conclude, therefore, that the differences are not significant and there are no grounds for rejecting the hypothesis. This means that we are justified in stating that the weights of Cambridge University rowing men in 1956 were normally distributed about a mean of 169 lb. with a standard deviation of 14·4 lb.

61. More precise interpretation of the P values. The various illustrations of the uses of the χ^2-distribution which follow will help to make clear the mathematical meaning of the P values. In the meantime table 6E is a descriptive treatment which will help in the interpretation of a value of χ^2 when it has been calculated. It indicates that, since the value of χ^2, 3·39, obtained in the last paragraph is considerably less than the $P = 10\%$ value, there is every reason to believe that the sample under consideration is from a normal population.

TABLE 6E
WHEN TO REJECT THE NULL HYPOTHESIS

If χ^2 is:	The differences between the observed and expected frequencies are:	The null hypothesis is:
Greater than $P = 5\%$ value	Significant	Probably false
Greater than $P = 2\cdot5\%$ value	Very significant	Very probably false
Greater than $P = 1\%$ value	Most significant	Almost certainly false

WHEN TO ACCEPT THE NULL HYPOTHESIS

If χ^2 is:	The differences between the observed and expected frequencies are:	The null hypothesis is:
Less than $P = 5\%$ value	Not significant	Probably true
Less than $P = 10\%$ value	Not in the least significant	Very probably true

WHEN χ^2 IS INCREDIBLY SMALL

If χ^2 is less than $P = 95\%$ value the agreement of the observed data with the null hypothesis is *almost too good to be true* and it leads us to suspect:

  (i) the sample is not random but carefully selected;
or (ii) the sample consists of fictitious data and is not the result of a proper statistical investigation;
or (iii) the null hypothesis may have been constructed in a ridiculously complicated way so as to suit the data too perfectly.

TABLE 6F
Weights of crews in the first and second divisions of the Cambridge University Lent Bumping Races, 1956, *with the weights of the coxes included*

Weight (lb.)	110–	120–	130–	140–	150–	160–	170–	180–	190–	200–	210–	220–
Frequency	3	14	14	24	49	65	72	29	11	5	0	2

62. A distribution which is not normal. Table 6F shows the distribution of the weights of the Cambridge University Lent boat crews with the weights of the coxes included. This raises the total number of men to 288, lowers the mean weight to 164·5 lb. and extends the standard deviation to 18·46 lb. An inspection of the distribution, or its histogram, reveals that it no longer seems normal. The calculation of $\chi^2 = 22\cdot39$ is shown in table 6G. As the number of classes in this case is 9 and the number of restrictions is again 3, the number of degrees of freedom $\nu = 6$. Reference to table A4 shows that χ^2 is greater than the $P = 0.5\%$ value and is almost equal to the $P = 0.1\%$ value. The differences between the observed and expected frequencies are, therefore, most significant and the null hypothesis that the distribution is normal must be rejected. Thus the inclusion of the weights of the coxes destroys completely the normality of the distribution.

TABLE 6G
Calculation of χ^2

Weight (lb.)	Observed frequency O	Expected frequency E	$O - E$	$\dfrac{(O-E)^2}{E}$ to 2 decimals
Less than 130	17	9	$+8$	7·11
130–	14	17	-3	0·53
140–	24	36	-12	4·00
150–	49	54	-5	0·46
160–	65	62	$+3$	0·15
170–	72	52	$+20$	7·70
180–	29	34	-5	0·75
190–	11	16	-5	1·56
200 and over	7	8	-1	0·13
Total	288	288	0	$22·39 = \chi^2$

The fact that χ^2 is greater than the $P = 0.5\%$ value means that the probability of obtaining a random sample with a distribution like that of table 6F from a normal population is less than $0.5/100 = \frac{1}{200}$. Since χ^2 is almost equal to the $P = 0.1\%$ value this last probability is almost $0.1/100 = \frac{1}{1000}$. This precise mathematical interpretation of the value of χ^2 gives definite meaning to the rather vague statement 'almost certainly false' of table 6E.

63. Exercises.

Test each of the following distributions for normality.

1. In estimating the valuation of a plantation of fir trees, the girths of the trees in a sample area of 500 trees were measured and tabulated with a 10 in. grouping interval as follows:

Girth (in.)	15–25	25–35	35–45	45–55	55–65	65–75	75–85
No. of trees	25	30	135	160	100	40	10

[London]

2.   *Chest girth of* 1000 *men* (*British*) *aged* 20

Chest girth (in.)	Frequency
Under 31	9
31–	66
33–	285
35–	400
37–	192
39–	39
41 and over	9
Total	1000

[SOURCE: Martin, *The Physique of Young Adult Males*]

3.   *Height of* 1000 *men* (*British*) *aged* 20

Height (in.)	Frequency
Under 63	41
63–	124
65–	262
67–	296
69–	190
71–	68
73 and over	19
Total	1000

[Same source as Ex. 2 above]

4.   *The frequency distribution of the weights of* 1000 *half-pound packets of tea delivered by an automatic packing machine*

Weight of packet of tea (oz.)	7·8–	7·9–	8·0–	8·1–	8·2–	8·3–8·4
Frequency	14	56	347	423	140	20

64. Testing a binomial distribution. Table 6H shows the *observed* and *expected* frequencies for an experiment in which 6 dice were thrown together 216 times. The expected frequencies are based on the assumption or null hypothesis that the distribution is binomial and the only restriction imposed in their calculation is that their total is made the same as that of the observed frequencies. The number of degrees of freedom available in calculating χ^2 is, therefore,

$$\nu = 4 \text{ classes} - 1 \text{ restriction}$$
$$= 3.$$

Since the value of χ^2, *5·84, is less than the* $P = 10\%$ *value 6·25 obtained from table* A4, *the null hypothesis is very probably true and it is safe to say that the distribution is binomial.*

TABLE 6H
Testing a binomial distribution

No. of sixes obtained when 6 dice are cast	Observed frequency (the result of an actual experiment) O	Expected frequency (based on the assumption or null hypothesis that the distribution is binomial) E	$(O-E)^2$ / E
0	77	$216(\frac{5}{6})^6 = 72$	0·35
1	84	$216.6(\frac{5}{6})^5 (\frac{1}{6}) = 87$	0·10
2	34	$216.15 (\frac{5}{6})^4 (\frac{1}{6})^2 = 43$	1·89
3 or more	21	$216 -$ above $= 14$	3·50
Total	216	216	$5·84 = \chi^2$

65. Exercises.

Use the χ^2 test to determine if the following distributions conform to the binomial law. (Note that in Ex. 1 and 2 the *means* and *totals* agree and, therefore, the number of restrictions is 2. In Ex. 3, 4, 5 only the totals agree and the number of restrictions is 1 as in §64.)

1. The distribution of §48, Ex. 2.

2. The distribution of §47.

3.

No. of sixes obtained when 8 dice are cast	0	1	2	3 or more	Total
Frequency		16	22	14	8	60

4.

No. of fives or sixes when 6 dice are cast	0	1	2	3	4 or more	Total
Frequency		16	36	32	28	8	120

5.

No. of heads when 5 coins are tossed	0	1	2	3	4	5	Total
Frequency	25	123	246	264	146	28	832

Exercises 4–6 above are the results of experiments carried out by the author. The student will find it amusing to carry out similar experiments himself.

66. Testing a Poisson distribution.

A company which manufactures tubes for television receivers conducted a test of a sample batch of 1000 tubes and recorded the number of faults in each tube in the following table:

No. of faults	0	1	2	3	4	5	6
Frequency	620	260	88	20	8	2	2

[London]

As the variance, 0·74, is approximately equal to the mean, $a = 0·55$, one might suspect that the distribution is Poissonian. Table 61 shows the calculation of χ^2. As the expected frequency of 4 or more faults is considerably less than 10 the last two classes have been combined.

TABLE 61

Testing a Poisson distribution

No. of faults	Observed frequency (results of the actual test) O	Expected frequency (based on the assumption or null hypothesis that distribution is Poissonian) E	$\dfrac{(O-E)^2}{E}$
0	620	$1000 \times e^{-a} = 577$	3·20
1	260	$1000 \times a e^{-a} = 317$	10·25
2	88	$1000 \times \tfrac{1}{2}a^2 e^{-a} = 87$	0·01
3	20⎫	$1000 \times \tfrac{1}{6}a^3 e^{-a} = 16$⎫	8·90
4 or more	12⎭	1000–above $= 3$⎭	
Total	1000	1000	$22 \cdot 36 = \chi^2$

In calculating the expected frequencies two restrictions have been imposed, in that their mean and total have been made equal respectively to the mean and total of the observed frequencies. Hence the number of degrees of freedom, ν, available in the calculation of χ^2, is

$$4 \text{ classes} - 2 \text{ restrictions} = 2.$$

On reference to table A4 we find $\chi^2 = 22 \cdot 36$ is greater than the $P = 0 \cdot 1 \%$ value and we infer that the observed frequencies differ very significantly from the expected frequencies. Therefore the null hypothesis that the distribution is Poissonian must be rejected.

67. A distribution may conform to both the binomial and the Poisson laws. As the Poisson distribution is a convenient alternative form of the binomial distribution when p is small and n is large many distributions will be found to conform to both laws. For example, the distribution of §64 (in which p has the comparatively small value of $\tfrac{1}{6}$ and n the comparatively large value of 6) does not differ significantly from the Poisson distribution with $a = 1$. Some of the exercises which follow are further illustrations of this point.

68. Exercises.

Use the χ^2-test to determine if the following distributions conform to the Poisson law.

1. The distribution of §55, Ex. 8.
2. The distribution of §55, Ex. 9.
3. The distribution of §55, Ex. 10.
4. The distribution of §48, Ex. 2.
5. The distribution of §47.
6. The distribution of §65, Ex. 3.
7. The distribution of §65, Ex. 4.
8. The distribution of §65, Ex. 5.

7

The use of χ^2 in testing Contingency Tables

69. Introductory experiment. Throwing a single die. The following table gives the frequency distribution obtained when a single die was cast 648 times.

Score	1	2	3	4	5	6
Frequency	96	98	117	130	107	100

If the die were unbiased the expected frequency of each score would be 108 since each number on the die would be equally probable. The χ^2-test can be used to decide if the observed frequencies differ significantly from the expected frequencies. The calculation of χ^2 is shown in table 7A.

TABLE 7A
Testing a die

Score	Observed frequencies (the result of an actual experiment) O	Expected frequencies (based on the assumption or null hypothesis that each score is equally probable) E	$\dfrac{(O-E)^2}{E}$
1	96	108	1·33
2	98	108	0·93
3	117	108	0·75
4	130	108	4·48
5	107	108	0·01
6	100	108	0·59
Total	648	648	$8·09 = \chi^2$

No. of degrees of freedom, $\nu = 6$ classes $- 1$ restriction (totals equal)
$$= 5.$$

As the value of χ^2, 8·09, is less than the $P = 10\%$ value, 9·24, we conclude that the differences between the observed and expected frequencies are not significant and we accept the null hypothesis that each score was equally probable in spite of the high frequency of the score 4.

70. An experiment with playing cards. After an ordinary pack of 52 playing cards comprising 4 suits of 13 spades, 13 hearts, 13 diamonds and 13 clubs had been well shuffled, a single card was drawn at random from it and the suit noted. This experiment was repeated 98 times and the following distribution obtained.

Suit	Spades	Hearts	Diamonds	Clubs
Frequency	23	31	20	24

The expected frequencies in this case were each $24\frac{1}{2}$ because the suits were equally probable for each random selection. The question arose: 'Had the differences in the frequencies some special significance or were they merely the fluctuations of experiment?' Table 7B shows the application of the χ^2-test.

TABLE 7B

Testing a pack of cards by selecting one card at random from the pack after it had been thoroughly shuffled

Suit	Observed frequencies O	Expected frequencies (based on the hypothesis that each suit was equally probable) E	$\dfrac{(O-E)^2}{E}$
Spades	23	$24\frac{1}{2}$	0·09
Hearts	31	$24\frac{1}{2}$	1·72
Diamonds	20	$24\frac{1}{2}$	0·83
Clubs	24	$24\frac{1}{2}$	0·01
Total	98	98	2·65 $= \chi^2$

No. of degrees of freedom, $v = 4$ classes $- 1$ restriction (totals equal)
$$= 3.$$

As the value of χ^2, 2·65, is less than the $P = 10\%$ value, 6·25, the differences were not significant but merely the normal fluctuations of experiment.

71. Contingency tables. When the classes in which frequencies are grouped are not class-intervals in a measured variate, but correspond to some attribute or descriptive quality the frequency table is called a *contingency table*. Section 70 provides a good introductory example of a contingency table. Other examples follow.

72. An example from an engineering workshop. In a certain workshop cutting tools of four types are in regular use and a record was kept for a period of 3 months of the number of breakages of each type. These are presented in table 7c together with the calculation of χ^2 based on the null hypothesis that, in spite of the observed variations in breakages, all four types of cutting tool are equally good.

TABLE 7C
Testing four different types of cutting tool

Type	Observed no. of breakages in 3 months O	Expected no. of breakages (based on the null hypothesis that all tools are equally good) E	$\dfrac{(O-E)^2}{E}$
1	21	$17\frac{1}{2}$	0·70
2	13	$17\frac{1}{2}$	1·16
3	20	$17\frac{1}{2}$	0·36
4	16	$17\frac{1}{2}$	0·13
Total	70	70	$2·35 = \chi^2$

No. of degrees of freedom, $\nu = 4$ classes $- 1$ restriction (totals equal)
$$= 3.$$

As χ^2 is less than the $P = 10\,\%$ value, 6·25, the differences are not significant and the null hypothesis is not rejected. We therefore conclude that the cutting tools are all equally good in spite of the variations in breakages.

TABLE 7D
Testing a pack of 30 *playing cards comprising* 12 *spades,* 9 *hearts,* 6 *diamonds,* 3 *clubs, by drawing at random one card from the pack after shuffling it*

Suit	Observed frequency (result of 'shuffling and drawing' 170 times) O	Expected frequency (based on the null hypothesis that the frequencies would be in the ratio 12:9:6:3) E	$\dfrac{(O-E)^2}{E}$
Spades	73	68	0·37
Hearts	49	51	0·08
Diamonds	32	34	0·12
Clubs	16	17	0·59
Total	170	170	$1·16 = \chi^2$

No. of degrees of freedom, $\nu = 4$ classes $- 1$ restriction (totals equal)
$$= 3.$$

73. Expected frequencies in a given ratio. The following experiment is interesting in that it produces a contingency table in which the expected frequencies are in the ratio 4:3:2:1. From an ordinary pack of 52 playing cards, 12 spades, 9 hearts, 6 diamonds and 3 clubs were taken to form a *special* little pack of 30 cards. After shuffling this *special* pack a card was drawn at random from it and its suit noted. This experiment was repeated 170 times. Table 7D presents the observed frequencies and the calculation of χ^2 based on the null hypothesis that the expected frequencies of spades, hearts, diamonds, clubs are in the ratio $12:9:6:3$. As χ^2 is less than the $P = 10\%$ value, the differences are not significant and the null hypothesis is upheld.

74. An example from genetic theory. *Genetic theory states that children having one parent of blood-type M and the other of blood-type N will always be one of the three types M, MN, N and the proportions of these types will on the average be as $1:2:1$. A report states 'of 162 children having one M parent and one N parent, $28\cdot4\%$ were found to be of type M, 42% of type MN and the remainder of type N. The low value of χ^2 demonstrates the truth of the genetic theory.' Calculate the value of χ^2, make the appropriate test of significance and comment on the conclusions quoted.* [R.S.S.]

The calculation, which is similar to that of §73, is shown in table 7E. The observed frequencies $28\cdot4\%$ of 162, 42% of 162, $29\cdot6\%$ of 162 are 46, 68, and 48 respectively. As χ^2 is less than the $P = 10\%$ value, $4\cdot62$, the null hypothesis is confirmed.

TABLE 7E

An example from genetic theory

Blood-type	Observed frequency O	Expected frequency (based on the null hypothesis that the proportions are $1:2:1$) E	$\dfrac{(O-E)^2}{E}$
M	46	$40\frac{1}{2}$	0·75
MN	68	81	2·09
N	48	$40\frac{1}{2}$	1·39
Total	162	162	$4\cdot23 = \chi^2$

No. of degrees of freedom, $\nu = 3$ classes $- 1$ restriction (totals equal)
$$= 2.$$

75. An example illustrating Yates's correction when $\nu = 1$. *A door-to-door salesman's records show that 25% of his calls are successful. After taking a course in salesmanship 12 of the first 30 calls he makes are successful. Is this definite proof that his technique is improved?*

The null hypothesis in this case is that the apparent improvement is a chance effect and that, in the long run, the man's proportion of successful calls will still be only 25%. The calculation of χ^2 is shown in table 7F. As there are only two classes and the totals are equal the

54

number of degrees of freedom is unity and it is necessary to apply *Yates's correction for continuity* which states that *when $v = 1$ the $(O - E)$ differences must each be diminished numerically by $\frac{1}{2}$.*

TABLE 7F

Calculation of χ^2 using Yates's correction when $v = 1$

	Observed frequencies O	Expected frequencies (based on the null hypothesis that 25% are successful) E	Yates's correction of $(O-E)$ $(O-E)$	Y	$\dfrac{Y^2}{E}$
Successes	12	$7\frac{1}{2}$	$4\frac{1}{2}$	4	2·14
Failures	18	$22\frac{1}{2}$	$-4\frac{1}{2}$	-4	0·71
Total	30	30	0	0	$2\cdot85 = \chi^2$

As the value of χ^2 is less than the $P = 5\%$ value, the differences are not significant. The null hypothesis is, therefore, not rejected and we conclude that there is no definite proof that the salesman's technique is improved.

76. Exercises.

1. While practising rifle shooting a man is successful with $\frac{1}{3}$ of his shots. After special coaching he achieves 19 successes with his first 40 shots. Use χ^2 to show that his marksmanship cannot be considered definitely improved.

If he were to go on shooting and obtain 38 successes with his first 80 shots would he then have proved himself a better shot?

2. Ten years ago the numbers of male and female office workers in a certain city were in the ratio 3:2. A recent random sample of 500 office workers revealed that 280 were men and 220 were women. Is this definite proof that the percentage of women office workers has increased?

3. A football pools expert claims that, over a long period, 50% of his forecasts have been correct. On a particular Saturday he has only 24 forecasts out of 64 correct. Does this indicate that his claim is probably false?

77. A 2 × 2 contingency table. The following table summarises the *infant mortality* and *overcrowding* figures of 100 districts.

TABLE 7G

		Overcrowding High	Low	Total
Infant mortality	High	22	15	37
	Low	14	49	63
Total		36	64	100

Thus, there are 22 districts in which the overcrowding is high and the infant mortality high, 15 in which the overcrowding is low and the infant mortality is high and so on. It is an example of a 2×2 contingency table. The question arises 'Does association exist between the two variables or are they completely independent?' Alternatively one might ask, 'Is a high infant mortality figure generally associated with a high overcrowding figure?'

Let us suppose that the variables are completely independent. A probability table can then be drawn up as shown in table 7H:

TABLE 7H

Overcrowding

		High	Low	Probability
Infant	High	$0\cdot36 \times 0\cdot37 = 0\cdot1332$	$0\cdot64 \times 0\cdot37 = 0\cdot2368$	0·37
mortality	Low	$0\cdot36 \times 0\cdot63 = 0\cdot2268$	$0\cdot64 \times 0\cdot63 = 0\cdot4032$	0·63
Probability		0·36	0·64	1

The marginal probabilities in the above table are obtained by dividing the marginal totals of the previous table by the total frequency 100. The marginal probabilities indicate that if any district is chosen at random from the 100 districts, the probability that it is highly overcrowded is 0·36 and the probability that its infant mortality is high is 0·37. Hence, if these probabilities are independent, the compound probability (see §22) of any district chosen at random having high overcrowding and high infant mortality figures is the product $0\cdot36 \times 0\cdot37$. Thus the probabilities in the four central *cells* are obtained from the marginal probabilities in the manner indicated.

The probability table can finally be converted into the table of expected frequencies (table 7I) by multiplying the probability in each *cell* by the total frequency 100.

TABLE 7I

Table of expected frequencies

(*Based on the null hypothesis that infant mortality and overcrowding are independent*)

Overcrowding

		High	Low	Total
Infant mortality	High	13·32	23·68	37·00
	Low	22·68	40·32	63·00
Total		36·00	64·00	100·00

The calculation of χ^2 is shown in table 7J. The number of degrees of freedom in a 2×2 table is unity. This is due to the fact that when one of the four values in the central cells is known the other three values can be obtained from the marginal totals which are the same in the O and E tables. Since $\nu = 1$ it is necessary to apply Yates's correction.

TABLE 7J

Observed frequencies O	Expected frequencies E	$(O-E)$	Yates's correction of $(O-E)$ Y	$\dfrac{Y^2}{E}$
22	13·32	8·68	8·18	5·02
15	23·68	−8·68	−8·18	2·83
14	22·68	−8·68	−8·18	2·95
49	40·32	8·68	8·18	1·66
Total 100	100·00	0·00	0·00	$12·46 = \chi^2$

As the value of χ^2 is greater than the $P = 0·1\,\%$ value the null hypothesis that the two variables are independent is rejected. Association between infant mortality and overcrowding is thus confirmed.

78. Experiments using coloured dice.

1. *Throwing two dice.*

TABLE 7K

		Black die score	
		1–3	4–6
White	{1–3	23	27
die score	{4–6	21	29

Table 7K is a 2×2 contingency table in which association should not exist. It was obtained by throwing together a black die and a white die and one would expect the score of the white die to be completely independent of that of the black die. Draw up a table of expected frequencies based on the null hypothesis that no association exists between the pairs of scores and show by calculating χ^2 that the null hypothesis is true.

Perform a similar experiment for yourself.

2. *Throwing three dice.*

TABLE 7L

		Score of black and white dice	
		2–6	7–12
Score of black and	{2–6	26	16
green dice	{7–12	14	44

Table 7L is a 2×2 contingency table in which association should exist. It was obtained by throwing together a black die, a white die and a green die and as the black score is common to both totals the pairs are not completely independent. Test the table in a similar way to experiment 1.

Perform a similar experiment for yourself.

79. Exercises.

1. *Place of midday meal of earners, Stepney, 1946*

Earners with weekly fares	At home	Elsewhere	Totals
2s. 9d. and under	355	120	475
Over 2s. 9d.	19	85	104
Total	374	205	579

(Source: unpublished material from a sample survey of Stepney.)

Assume that the sample is a random one from a large population. Is it possible that there was no association between the place of midday meal and fares in Stepney?   [London]

2. A certain type of surgical operation can be performed either with a local anaesthetic or with a general anaesthetic. Results are as given below:

	Alive	Dead
Local	511	24
General	173	21

Test for any difference in the mortality rates associated with the different types of anaesthetic.   [R.S.S.]

3. The following information was obtained in a sample of 50 small general shops:

	Shops in		
	Urban districts	Rural districts	Total
Owned by men	17	18	35
Owned by women	3	12	15
Total	20	30	50

Can it be said that there are relatively more women owners of small general shops in rural than in urban districts?   [London]

4. *Cigarette smoking and lung cancer*

	Death due to	
	Lung cancer	Other causes
Heavy smokers	27	11
Light smokers	18	44

Do the above figures suggest that heavy smokers are more likely to die from cancer of the lung than light smokers?

(NOTE. This exercise is set as an example of the technique. The figures are not from any official source.)

5.   *Greenwood and Yule's data on inoculation against typhoid*

	Attacked	Not attacked	Total
Inoculated	56	6,759	6,815
Not inoculated	272	11,396	11,668
Total	328	18,155	18,483

Do the above figures indicate that inoculation is a good preventative against typhoid?

80. The h × k contingency table.

The method used for the 2×2 contingency table can be extended for use with a table which has h rows and k columns where h and k are both greater than 1. Since the marginal totals of E's and O's are made to agree the number of degrees of freedom in this case is

$$\nu = (h-1)(k-1),$$

because the last row and last column are determined once the remaining cells have been filled.

Table 7M shows the application of the χ^2-test to a 3×3 classification of the examination results in Pure Mathematics and Applied Mathematics of 200 candidates.

TABLE 7M

(i) The observed frequencies

		Pure Mathematics			
		Good	Pass	Fail	Total
Applied Mathematics	Good	16	13	10	39
	Pass	20	33	16	69
	Fail	10	28	54	92
Total		46	74	80	200

(ii) The expected frequencies (based on the assumption of no association)

		Pure Mathematics			
		Good	Pass	Fail	Total
Applied Mathematics	Good	$\frac{39}{200} \times \frac{46}{200} \times 200$	$\frac{39}{200} \times \frac{74}{200} \times 200$	$\frac{39}{200} \times \frac{80}{200} \times 200$	$\frac{39}{200} \times 200$
	Pass	$\frac{69}{200} \times \frac{46}{200} \times 200$	$\frac{69}{200} \times \frac{74}{200} \times 200$	$\frac{69}{200} \times \frac{80}{200} \times 200$	$\frac{69}{200} \times 200$
	Fail	$\frac{92}{200} \times \frac{46}{200} \times 200$	$\frac{92}{200} \times \frac{74}{200} \times 200$	$\frac{92}{200} \times \frac{80}{200} \times 200$	$\frac{92}{200} \times 200$
Total		$\frac{46}{200} \times 200$	$\frac{74}{200} \times 200$	$\frac{80}{200} \times 200$	200

(iii) The calculation of χ^2

O	16	13	10	20	33	16	10	28	54	
E	9·0	14·4	15·6	15·8	25·6	27·6	21·2	34·0	36·8	Total
$(O-E)^2/E$	8·04	1·06	5·92	4·88	2·14	1·12	2·01	0·14	5·44	$30·76 = \chi^2$

(iv) The number of degrees of freedom $h = k = 3$

$$\nu = (h-1)(k-1)$$
$$= 4.$$

As the value of χ^2 is greater than the $P = 0.1\%$ value, 18.47, the differences between the O's and E's are highly significant and the assumption of no association must be rejected. Therefore, one concludes, as might be expected, that association almost certainly exists between a candidate's results in Pure Mathematics and Applied Mathematics.

81. Exercises.

1.

Throwing two dice

Black die score

		1 or 2	3 or 4	5 or 6
White die score	1 or 2	12	14	11
	3 or 4	17	9	9
	5 or 6	7	9	12

Show, by calculating χ^2, that no association exists between the pairs of scores in the above 3×3 table.

Perform a similar experiment for yourself.

2. *Relationship between number of wage-earners and output per manshift at coal mines employing* 100 *or more wage-earners in Great Britain in 1945*

Size of mine	No. of mines with an output per manshift of				
No. of wage-earners	Under 15 cwt.	15 cwt. and under 20 cwt.	20 cwt. and under 25 cwt.	25 cwt. and over	Total mines
100–499	103	140	76	42	361
500–999	58	131	76	39	304
1000 and over	25	73	83	48	229
Total mines	186	344	235	129	894

(Source: Ministry of Fuel and Power, *Statistical Digest*, 1945.)

By calculating χ^2 show that there is association between the number of wage-earners employed in a mine and the output per manshift in that mine.

[London]

3. *Brownlee's data on severity of smallpox attack*

Years since vaccination took place	Severity of attack				
	Very severe	Severe	Moderate	Light	Total
0–25	43	120	176	148	487
25–45	184	299	268	181	932
Over 45 or unvaccinated	111	89	40	30	270
Total	338	508	484	359	1689

Calculate χ^2 for the above 3×4 table and use it to demonstrate that association exists between severity of smallpox attack and the years that have elapsed since vaccination.

8

Samples and Significance

82. Sample estimates of population values. As an illustration of the use of a *random sample* to estimate the properties of the *parent population* from which the sample is drawn, consider the following example.

The following observations are heights in inches of a random sample of twenty compression springs taken from a current production in a works:

1·010	1·002	1·009	1·005	1·006
1·002	1·007	1·007	1·011	1·002
1·007	1·008	1·003	1·002	1·001
1·007	1·005	1·000	1·008	1·008

Calculate the mean and standard deviation of these observations and hence estimate the mean and standard deviation of the complete population of springs produced in the works.

If the distribution is normal, what is the probability that the height of any spring selected at random is

(i)   *more than* 1·010 *in.;*

(ii) *more than* 1·015 *in.;*

(iii) *more than* 0·010 *in. from the mean?*

To distinguish clearly between the mean and standard deviation of a sample and the corresponding parameters of its parent population English small italic letters are used for the sample values and the corresponding small Greek letters for the population values. Thus m and s are used to denote the mean and standard deviation of the sample while μ and σ are used to denote the mean and standard deviation of the parent population.

For a sample of n values $x_1, x_2, x_3, \ldots, x_n$, the mean m calculated in the usual way by

$$m = \frac{1}{n}\{x_1 + x_2 + x_3 + \ldots + x_n\}$$

$$= \frac{1}{n}\Sigma x$$

gives a good estimate of μ and we write

$$m = \frac{1}{n}\Sigma x = \text{Est}(\mu).$$

The usual way of calculating s by

$$s = \sqrt{\left\{\frac{(x_1-m)^2+(x_2-m)^2+(x_3-m)^2+\ldots+(x_n-m)^2}{n}\right\}}$$

$$= \sqrt{\left\{\frac{\Sigma(x-m)^2}{n}\right\}}$$

$$= \sqrt{\left\{\frac{\Sigma x^2}{n}-\left(\frac{\Sigma x}{n}\right)^2\right\}}$$

does not give such a good estimate of σ as the value of s obtained by

$$s = \sqrt{\left\{\frac{(x_1-m)^2+(x_2-m)^2+(x_3-m)^2+\ldots+(x_n-m)^2}{(n-1)}\right\}}$$

$$= \sqrt{\left\{\frac{\Sigma(x-m)^2}{(n-1)}\right\}}$$

$$= \sqrt{\left\{\frac{\Sigma x^2}{(n-1)}-\frac{n}{(n-1)}\left(\frac{\Sigma x}{n}\right)^2\right\}}.$$

The reason for this cannot be given here except to state that $(n-1)$ represents the number of degrees of freedom available for calculating s. Thus

$$s = \sqrt{\left\{\frac{\Sigma(x-m)^2}{(n-1)}\right\}} = \text{Est}(\sigma).$$

It is obvious that the use of the correct divisor $(n-1)$ for estimating σ is only important when n is small. For a large sample containing, say, 50 items, the difference between the estimates of σ obtained by divisors 50 and 49 will be negligible.

Returning now to the sample of 20 compression springs it is helpful to rewrite the heights in thousandths of an inch with 1·005 in. as origin, thus:

5	−3	4	0	1
−3	2	2	6	−3
2	3	−2	−3	−4
2	0	−5	3	3

The estimate of the population mean, $\text{Est}(\mu)$, is then

$$m = \tfrac{1}{20}\Sigma x$$

$$= \tfrac{1}{20}\{5-3+4+\ldots+3\}$$

$$= 0\cdot5 \text{ thousandths with } 1\cdot005 \text{ in. as origin}$$

$$= 1\cdot0055 \text{ in.,}$$

and the estimate of the population standard deviation, $\text{Est}(\sigma)$, is

$$s = \sqrt{\left\{\frac{\Sigma x^2}{19} - \frac{20}{19}\left(\frac{\Sigma x}{20}\right)^2\right\}}$$

$$= \sqrt{\left\{\frac{202}{19} - \frac{20}{19}(0\cdot5)^2\right\}}$$

$$= 3\cdot22 \text{ thousandths}$$

$$= 0\cdot00322 \text{ in.}$$

To answer question (i) it should be noted that a spring of height 1·010 in. has a *standardized deviate* from the mean of

$$\frac{(1\cdot010 - 1\cdot0055)}{0\cdot00322} = 1\cdot397$$

and by table A2, $A(1\cdot397) = 0\cdot9188$. Thus the probability of any spring being of greater height than 1·010 in. is

$$1 - A(1\cdot397) = 0\cdot0812$$

$$= \tfrac{1}{12} \text{ approximately.}$$

Similarly to answer question (ii), a spring of height 1·015 in. has a standardized deviate of

$$\frac{1\cdot015 - 1\cdot0055}{0\cdot00322} = 2\cdot95$$

and $A(2\cdot95) = 0\cdot9984$. Hence the probability of a spring being of greater height than 1·015 in. is 0·0016 or $\tfrac{1}{625}$.

Finally to answer question (iii) it should be noted that a height which is 0·010 in. from the mean has a standardized deviate of

$$\frac{0\cdot010}{0\cdot00322} = 3\cdot106.$$

Since $A(3\cdot106) = 0\cdot99905$, the probability that any spring has a height of more than 0·010 in. *above* the mean is 0·00095. Further, the probability that any spring has a height of more than 0·010 in. *below* the mean is also 0·00095 and hence the *total* probability that any spring has a height more than 0·010 in. from the mean is 0·00190 or approximately $\tfrac{1}{500}$.

83. Two-tail probability. Question (iii) above provides an example of a *two-tail* probability. The answers to questions (i), (ii) and (iii) are illustrated diagrammatically by fig. 8 in which the total area under the graph is supposed to be unity and the areas JKB, LMB and PQB are supposed to be 0·0812, 0·0016 and 0·00095 respectively although they are not actually drawn to scale.

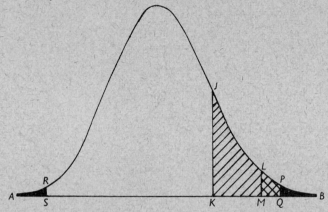

Fig. 8. Illustration of probabilities (i), (ii) and (iii) of §82 (not to scale). (i) Area JKB is the probability of the height of any spring being more than 1·010 in. (ii) Area LMB is the probability of the height of any spring being more than 1·015 in. (iii) The sum of the areas of the two tails ARS and PQB is the probability of the height of any spring being more than 0·010 in. from the mean.

84. Exercises.

Estimate the mean and standard deviation of the parent populations from which the following samples are drawn:

1. Accurate weights in ounces of 11 1 lb. cartons of sugar delivered by an automatic packing machine

16·17	16·51	16·78	15·96	16·33	16·59
16·14	16·40	16·72	15·98	16·82	

2. Ten measurements, in inches, of the thickness of the lead cover of a submarine cable

0·24　0·26　0·28　0·20　0·22　0·23　0·25　0·27　0·29　0·21

85. The frequency distribution of means of samples.

If observations are collected, not individually, but as random samples of n, a frequency distribution can be constructed for the means of the samples. It is customary to represent the mean and standard deviation of this frequency distribution of sample-means as μ_n and σ_n respectively. Now it can be shown theoretically that

$$\mu_n = \mu$$

but
$$\sigma_n = \sigma/\sqrt{n},$$

where μ and σ are the mean and standard deviation of the individual observations.

TABLE 8A
Cambridge University Boat Club. Weights of crews, in lb.
(to nearest lb.), in the Lent Bumping Races, 1956

	Bow	2	3	4	5	6	7	Str.	Mean weight
First Division									
Jesus 1	148	168	168	174	172	185	174	174	170·4
1st and 3rd Trinity 1	160	171	178	157	178	183	168	168	170·4
L.M.B.C. 1	161	162	171	173	156	181	168	155	165·9
Peterhouse 1	171	168	176	169	196	175	157	171	172·9
Pembroke 1	146	152	160	170	190	190	169	173	168·8
Emmanuel 1	145	169	165	174	199	182	178	170	172·8
Clare 1	154	144	178	194	168	187	144	154	165·4
Trinity Hall 1	163	165	168	171	184	172	169	184	172·0
King's 1	161	146	170	173	166	161	172	160	163·6
Corpus Christi 1	147	160	161	153	174	187	152	150	160·5
Magdalene 1	183	179	174	175	209	190	196	175	185·1
Jesus 2	173	164	178	169	209	164	154	145	169·5
Queen's 1	150	171	176	182	178	176	175	171	172·4
Christ's 1	148	168	176	178	183	186	170	159	171·0
Caius 1	161	165	173	182	186	176	177	202	177·8
St Catherine's 1	143	169	174	171	181	167	168	146	164·9
Second Division									
1st and 3rd Trinity 2	146	147	164	168	170	158	154	154	157·6
St Catherine's 2	156	164	178	148	182	158	186	154	165·8
Selwyn 1	164	160	159	193	188	158	164	185	171·4
L.M.B.C. 2	158	163	164	179	178	172	177	163	169·0
Downing 1	141	157	154	185	191	178	168	166	167·5
Sidney Sussex 1	152	154	189	176	177	189	187	189	176·6
Clare 2	178	147	170	151	189	170	182	156	167·9
Trinity Hall 2	161	150	160	178	173	175	161	162	165·0
Jesus 3	158	163	159	168	164	178	172	161	165·4
Fitzwilliam 1	156	181	203	208	169	190	151	155	176·6
Pembroke 2	162	156	177	166	195	175	153	147	166·4
Peterhouse 2	150	140	157	184	220	169	140	171	166·4
1st and 3rd Trinity 3	154	160	162	174	159	178	161	146	161·8
Emmanuel 2	150	136	149	185	150	224	164	152	163·8
Caius 2	154	158	161	178	171	166	174	147	163·6
King's 2	152	156	173	167	159	163	170	136	159·5

Mean weight by grouping = 168·8 lb.⎫ See table 6A
Standard deviation by grouping = 14·44 lb.⎭
(using Sheppard's correction)
Mean of the mean weights = 168·4 lb.
Standard deviation of the mean weights = 5·40 lb.

A numerical illustration of this important theorem is provided by table 8A which gives the individual weights of 256 oarsmen divided into 32 samples of 8, the mean weight of each sample being given in the final column.

The mean and standard deviation of the 256 individual weights are

$$\mu = 168 \cdot 8 \text{ lb.},$$

$$\sigma = 14 \cdot 44 \text{ lb.}$$

The mean and standard deviation of the 32 sample-means are

$$\mu_8 = 168 \cdot 4 \text{ lb.},$$

$$\sigma_8 = 5 \cdot 40 \text{ lb.}$$

But $$\sigma/\sqrt{8} = 14 \cdot 44/2 \cdot 828 \text{ lb.},$$

$$= 5 \cdot 12 \text{ lb.}$$

Thus table 8 A gives an approximate verification of the general theorem for the case when $n = 8$.

86. Standard error and fiducial limits of large samples. Suppose we have a single sample of n observations (n large). We may regard its mean m and standard deviation s as estimates of μ and σ, the mean and standard deviation of the parent population. Now $\sigma/\sqrt{n}$ is the standard deviation of the means of a large number of samples of n observations similar to our single sample. We can thus regard our single sample as one of many whose means are distributed with standard deviation $s/\sqrt{n}$ about a mean m, s being our estimate of σ. Moreover it can be shown that even when the distribution of the whole population is far from normal the distribution of the sample-means will be approximately normal. Thus, by the normal distribution table A2, 95 % of the sample-means will be spread over a range $1 \cdot 96 \times s/\sqrt{n}$ on either side of the mean. Thus *it is reasonably certain that the true value of the mean lies between*

$$m - 1 \cdot 96 s/\sqrt{n} \quad \text{and} \quad m + 1 \cdot 96 s/\sqrt{n}.$$

These limits are known as the 95 % *fiducial limits* and $s/\sqrt{n}$ is called the *standard error of the mean*.

A mathematical interpretation of the phrase 'it is reasonably certain that' is:

The probability of the true mean being outside the range $m \pm 1 \cdot 96 s/\sqrt{n}$ is $0 \cdot 05$ or $\frac{1}{20}$.

Further reference to table A2 shows that 99·8 % of the sample-means lie between $m - 3 \cdot 09 s/\sqrt{n}$ and $m + 3 \cdot 09 s/\sqrt{n}$. These, therefore, are the 99·8 % *fiducial limits* and the probability of the true mean being outside them is $0 \cdot 002$ or $\frac{1}{500}$.

Fiducial limits are often called *confidence limits*.

87. Use of the t-distribution for small samples. Consider once again §84, Ex. 1, which is a sample of 11 cartons of sugar for which

$$m = 16.40 \text{ oz.}, \quad s = 0.311 \text{ oz.}$$

and the number of degrees of freedom available for the calculation of s is $\nu = 10$. This is an example of a small sample for which it is necessary to use the percentage points of the t-distribution given in table A5 instead of the normal distribution. For $\nu = 10$, the $P = 5\%$ value of the t-distribution is found to be 2·23. This means that the 95% fiducial limits are $\quad m \pm 2.23s/\sqrt{n} = 16.40 \pm 2.23 \times 0.311/\sqrt{11}$

$$= 16.40 \pm 0.21.$$

Thus there is a probability of $\frac{1}{20}$ of the mean of the whole output of the automatic packing machine being outside the range 16·19 to 16·61 oz.

It will be noticed that, as ν increases indefinitely, the $P = 5\%$ and $P = 0.2\%$ values of the t-distribution approach the values 1·96 and 3·09 used in §86 for large samples.

88. Exercises.

1. (a) Obtain the 99·8% fiducial limits for §84, Ex. 1.
   (b) What is the probability of the mean of the whole output being between 16·25 and 16·55?

2. (a) Obtain the 99·9% fiducial limits of the mean thickness of the lead cover of §84, Ex. 2.
   (b) What is the probability of another sample of 10 measurements having a mean (i) outside the limits 0.245 ± 0.012, (ii) greater than 0·257?

3. From a large consignment of glass bottles a random sample of 400 bottles is drawn, their volumes being measured. The mean and standard deviation of these volumes are 507·3 c.c. and 8·2 c.c. respectively. Estimate the standard error of the mean and hence derive limits which have a 49 to 1 chance of including the mean volume of the whole consignment. How big would a sample have to be to make such limits differ by 1 c.c., the sample being drawn from a consignment with the same standard deviation as before?

[Northern]

89. The significance of a single mean (large samples). In §86 we saw that, for large samples, the probability of the true mean μ being outside the range $m \pm 1.96s/\sqrt{n}$ is $\frac{1}{20}$. This is equivalent to saying that the probability of

$$\frac{|\mu - m|}{s/\sqrt{n}}$$

being greater than 1·96 is $\frac{1}{20}$. Thus *the mean m of a large sample is said to differ significantly from a given value μ if*

$$\frac{|\mu - m|}{s/\sqrt{n}} > 1.96.$$

The difference between μ and m in this case is said to be *at the 5 % level of significance.*

If
$$\frac{|\mu - m|}{s/\sqrt{n}} > 3 \cdot 09$$

the difference between μ and m is at the 0·2 % level of significance; that is to say *very significant indeed* because the probability of the mean of a sample differing from the true mean by an amount large enough to make this possible is $\frac{1}{500}$.

90. Example. *The average breaking strength of steel rods is specified as 20 thousand lb. The breaking strengths of 100 rods when measured are found to have a mean of 19·9 thousand lb. with a standard deviation of 0·4 thousand lb. Is a complaint that the rods are not up to specification statistically justified?*

Taking $\mu = 20$, $m = 19\cdot9$, $s = 0\cdot4$ and $n = 100$,

$$\frac{|\mu - m|}{s/\sqrt{n}} = \frac{0\cdot1\sqrt{100}}{0\cdot4}$$
$$= 2\cdot5.$$

Thus the mean of the sample differs significantly from the specified average and the complaint that the rods are not up to specification is justified.

91. Exercises.

1. A machine producing components to a nominal dimension of 2·000 in. is reset every morning. The first 50 components produced one morning have a mean of 2·001 in. with standard deviation 0·003 in. Does this provide sufficient evidence that the machine is set too high?

2. Suppose that in the example of §90 only 50 rods had been tested and that the mean and standard deviation were the same. Would the complaint be justified?

3. Suppose that in the example of §90 100 rods were tested and that although the mean was the same 19·9 thousand lb. the standard deviation was 0·6 thousand lb. Would the complaint be justified?

92. The significance of a single mean (small samples). The significance of the mean, m, of a small sample is tested by comparing

$$t = \frac{|\mu - m|}{s/\sqrt{n}}$$

with the percentage points of the t-distribution given in table A 5. As in §89, μ is the mean of the whole population of which the sample is assumed to be a part. It will be noticed that the percentage points of the

t-distribution depend on the number of degrees of freedom, v, which are available for the calculation of the estimated standard deviation of the whole population and by §82

$$v = n-1.$$

The following example illustrates the method of applying the t-test. *Large samples of male and female plants of dog's mercury were collected at each of 13 sites in Derbyshire. The mean numbers of leaf pairs in these samples were as follows:*

Site	1	2	3	4	5	6	7	8	9	10	11	12	13
Male	6·0	6·6	8·0	7·0	6·4	6·9	6·1	6·9	6·6	8·2	7·9	7·0	7·5
Female	5·8	7·3	6·6	6·7	6·3	6·2	6·1	7·3	6·0	6·7	8·2	6·0	6·5

Find the differences between the mean numbers of leaf pairs of male and female plants from site to site, and calculate the mean and the standard deviation of these differences.

State whether or not these data can be taken to establish a real difference between the average numbers of leaf pairs for male and female plants. [Northern]

The required differences are:

0·2, −0·7, 1·4, 0·3, 0·1, 0·7, 0·0, −0·4, 0·6, 1·5, −0·3, 1·0, 1·0.

The mean of these differences is

$$m = 5·4/13$$
$$= 0·4154$$

and the standard deviation, which is an estimate of the standard deviation, σ, of the whole population of differences,

$$s = \sqrt{(5·697/12)}$$
$$= 0·6891.$$

If we assume that there is no real difference between the average numbers of leaf pairs for male and female plants we should expect the mean of the differences to be zero. We therefore take

$$\mu = 0, \ m = 0·4154, \ s = 0·6891, \ n = 13$$

and obtain

$$t = \frac{|\mu - m|}{s/\sqrt{n}}$$
$$= 2·173.$$

By table A5, when $v = 12$, the $P = 5\%$ value of t is 2·18. As the calculated value of t, 2·173, is not greater than the $P = 5\%$ value the mean of the differences does not differ significantly from zero. This means that the data cannot be taken to establish a real difference between the average numbers of leaf pairs for male and female plants.

Note that the value of t is so near to the $P = 5\%$ value that further investigation seems desirable. If collections were to be made at a greater number of sites, say 21 altogether, and the mean and standard deviation were found to be unaltered, a real difference would then be established because the value of t would be $0\cdot4154\sqrt{21}/0\cdot6891$ and the $P = 5\%$ value of the t-distribution when $\nu = 20$ is $2\cdot09$.

93. Exercises.

1. The average breaking strength of steel rods is specified as 20 thousand lb. A random sample of 10 rods had the following breaking strengths (in thousands of lb.):

$$23 \quad 21 \quad 16 \quad 24 \quad 19 \quad 22 \quad 25 \quad 19 \quad 18 \quad 24$$

Investigate the significance of the mean.

2. A machine producing components to a nominal dimension of $1\cdot125$ is reset each morning. The first half-hour's production one morning is:

$1\cdot125 \quad 1\cdot127 \quad 1\cdot131 \quad 1\cdot124 \quad 1\cdot128 \quad 1\cdot126 \quad 1\cdot126 \quad 1\cdot127 \quad 1\cdot132 \quad 1\cdot128 \quad 1\cdot124 \quad 1\cdot126.$

Does this provide real evidence that the machine is set high?

94. The variance of the sums = the sum of the variances. The variance of the differences = the SUM of the variances.

Suppose we have 4 red cards numbered 6, 7, 9, 10 and 3 black cards numbered 1, 3, 5. If we select at random 1 red card and 1 black the 12 possible pairs of numbers we might obtain are:

6 and 1, 6 and 3, 6 and 5, 7 and 1, 7 and 3, 7 and 5, 9 and 1,
9 and 3, 9 and 5, 10 and 1, 10 and 3, 10 and 5.

Now the mean and variance of the 4 *red numbers* are 8 and 10/4 respectively and the mean and variance of the 3 *black numbers* are 3 and 8/3 respectively. Note that in this case we are not estimating the variance of a population from that of a sample and therefore we use $\Sigma\{(x-\bar{x})^2/n\}$ and not $\Sigma\{(x-\bar{x})^2/(n-1)\}$. Further, the mean of the sums of the pairs of numbers is

$$\tfrac{1}{12}\{7+9+11+8+10+12+10+12+14+11+13+15\} = 11$$

and the variance is

$$\tfrac{1}{12}\{16+4+0+9+1+1+1+1+9+0+4+16\} = \tfrac{62}{12}.$$

Thus   *the mean of the sums = the sum of the means*

and   *the variance of the sums = the sum of the variances.*

Also, the mean of the differences of the pairs of numbers is

$$\tfrac{1}{12}\{5+3+1+6+4+2+8+6+4+9+7+5\} = 5$$

and the variance is

$$\tfrac{1}{12}\{0+4+16+1+1+9+9+1+1+16+4+0\} = \tfrac{62}{12}.$$

Thus *the mean of the differences = the difference of the means*

and *the variance of the differences = the SUM of the variances.*

The above special cases are examples of two important general theorems which may be stated as follows:

If the mean and variance of the m values $x_1, x_2, x_3, \ldots, x_m$ are $\bar{x}$ and s_x^2 and the mean and variance of the n values $y_1, y_2, y_3, \ldots, y_n$ are $\bar{y}$ and s_y^2 then (i) the mean and variance of the mn values of z given by $z = x+y$ are $\bar{x}+\bar{y}$ and $s_x^2+s_y^2$, and (ii) the mean and variance of the mn values of z given by $z = x-y$ are $\bar{x}-\bar{y}$ and $s_x^2+s_y^2$.

95. Experiment with two coloured dice. If a single die is thrown a large number of times the scores 1, 2, 3, 4, 5, 6 are all equally probable and the mean score will therefore approximate to

$$\tfrac{1}{6}\{1+2+3+4+5+6\} = 3\tfrac{1}{2}. \tag{1}$$

While the variance of the scores will approximate to

$$\tfrac{1}{6}\{6\tfrac{1}{4}+2\tfrac{1}{4}+\tfrac{1}{4}+\tfrac{1}{4}+2\tfrac{1}{4}+6\tfrac{1}{4}\} = 2\tfrac{11}{12}. \tag{2}$$

If a white die and a black die are thrown together a large number of times and a record is kept of

(a) the white score + the black score for each throw,
(b) the white score − the black score for each throw,

§94 leads us to expect

the mean of the sums (a) = 7, (3)
the variance of the sums (a) = $5\tfrac{5}{6}$, (4)
the mean of the differences (b) = 0, (5)
the variance of the differences (b) = $5\tfrac{5}{6}$. (6)

The facts of (1), (2), (3), (4), (5) and (6) above should be tested experimentally by throwing a single die

(i) 10 times, (ii) 50 times, (iii) 100 times,

and by throwing a pair of differently coloured dice

(i) 10 times, (ii) 50 times, (iii) 100 times.

96. Three or more dice. If the ideas of §§94 and 95 are extended to the mean and variance of the total score when three or more dice are thrown together the results shown in table 8B hold:

TABLE 8B

No. of dice thrown together	Mean score	Variance of scores	Standard deviation of scores
1	$3\frac{1}{2}$	$2\frac{11}{12}$	1·708
2	7	$5\frac{5}{6}$	2·416
3	$10\frac{1}{2}$	$8\frac{3}{4}$	2·958
4	14	$11\frac{2}{3}$	3·416
5	$17\frac{1}{2}$	$14\frac{7}{12}$	3·819

An important generalisation of the above is:

If $x_1, x_2, x_3, \ldots, x_n$ are n statistically independent variables

(i) *the mean of $(x_1+x_2+x_3+\ldots+x_n)$ = mean of x_1+mean of x_2+mean of x_3+…+mean of x_n,*

(ii) *the variance of $(x_1+x_2+x_3+\ldots+x_n)$ = variance of x_1+variance of x_2+variance of x_3+…+variance of x_n.*

A practical application follows.

97. Example. *In a certain workshop electrical resistances of three types are manufactured. Type A has a mean resistance of 50 ohms and standard deviation 2 ohms, type B a mean resistance of 10 ohms and standard deviation 0·5 ohms, type C a mean resistance of 5 ohms and standard deviation 0·3 ohms, each type being normally distributed about its mean. Resistances of approximately 85 ohms are then constructed by connecting in series one of type A, three of type B and one of type C. The resistances so constructed can be accepted only if accurate measurement shows them to be between 80 and 90 ohms; otherwise they must be rejected. Calculate the percentage likely to be rejected. Show further that the probability that any one of the resistances is between 84 and 86 ohms is slightly more than $\frac{1}{3}$.* [Northern]

The mean of the sum of the resistances $= 50+10+10+10+5$
$$= 85$$
and the variance of the sum $= 2^2+(0·5)^2+(0·5)^2+(0·5)^2+(0·3)^2$
$$= 4·84.$$

Thus the standard deviation of the sum $= 2·2$ and the standardized deviate of 80 or 90 from the mean is $5/2·2 = 2·273$. Now, by table A2, $A(2·273) = 0·98849$ and hence the percentage of 85 ohm resistances below 80 ohms or above 90 ohms is $100 - 98 \cdot 849 = 1 \cdot 151$. Thus the percentage likely to be rejected is $2 \cdot 30$.

Further, the standardized deviate of 84 or 86 from the mean is $1/2 \cdot 2 = 0 \cdot 4545$ and since $A(0 \cdot 4545) = 0 \cdot 6752$ it follows that $17 \cdot 52 \%$ of the resistances are between 85 and 86 and $17 \cdot 52 \%$ between 84 and 85. Thus $35 \cdot 04 \%$ are between 84 and 86 and this is equivalent to the statement that the probability of any one of the resistances being between 84 and 86 ohms is slightly more than $\frac{1}{3}$.

98. Exercises.

1. A certain firm mass-produced machines which, in the course of their assembly, passed through four workshops, A, B, C and D. A record of the times taken in each workshop and the times of transit from one workshop to the next was kept and from it the following summary showing the means and standard deviations of the times was published:

	Mean time (hr.)	Standard deviation (hr.)
Workshop A	3·48	0·25
Transit from A to B	0·23	0·05
Workshop B	4·56	0·30
Transit from B to C	0·53	0·12
Workshop C	1·91	0·20
Transit from C to D	0·32	0·10
Workshop D	2·67	0·20

Assuming that the workshop and transit times were independently normally distributed, calculate the mean and standard deviation of the times taken for the complete assembly of the machines, and show that only 1 % of the machines were assembled in less than $12\frac{1}{2}$ hr. while 6 % took over $14\frac{1}{2}$ hr. [Northern]

2. Four athletes specialize in running 220 yd., 220 yd., 440 yd. and 880 yd. respectively. They train as a team for a one-mile medley relay race. During training their mean times for their respective distances are 23·9 sec., 24·1 sec., 53·6 sec. and 2 min. 7·4 sec., and the corresponding standard deviations are 0·3 sec., 0·3 sec., 0·8 sec. and 1·8 sec. Assuming that their individual times are normally and independently distributed, estimate the mean and standard deviation of the times in which the team covers the mile. Also estimate the probability that, on any particular occasion, the time will be 3 min. 45 sec. or less. [Northern]

3. At the assembly stage in the manufacture of a knitting machine, four sections of bakelite of lengths x_1, x_2, x_3, x_4 are drawn at random from a box containing a large number of these sections and fitted between two pieces of metal on the partially assembled machine, these being separated by a distance y as shown in the diagram. The fit is considered satisfactory if the clearance $y - x_1 - x_2 - x_3 - x_4$ lies between zero and 0·10 in. (see fig. 9).

73

If the lengths of the pieces in the box vary randomly about a mean of 4·00 in. with a standard deviation of 0·015 in., and if y varies randomly from machine to machine with mean 16·06 in. and standard deviation 0·024 in. find the mean and standard deviation of the distribution of $y-x_1-x_2-x_3-x_4$.

Hence determine the proportion of assemblies giving a satisfactory fit at the first attempt. [Northern]

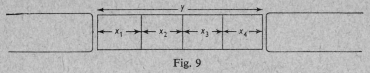

Fig. 9

99. Var $(a_1x_1+a_2x_2+\ldots+a_nx_n) = a_1^2\,\mathbf{var}\,x_1+a_2^2\,\mathbf{var}\,x_2+\ldots+a_n^2\,\mathbf{var}\,x_n$.
The following example extends still further the general principles of §96.

Three dice, each numbered in the usual way from one to six, are coloured white, red and blue respectively. After casting them a boy 'scores' in the following way. To the white number he adds twice the red number and then subtracts the blue number. Thus a white three, a red four and a blue two would score $$3+8-2 = 9.$$

Assuming that the boy casts the dice a large number of times calculate the mean and variance of the scores. [Northern]

Representing the white number by x_1, the red by x_2 and the blue by x_3, the method of scoring is
$$x_1+2x_2-x_3.$$

Now it can be proved mathematically that if x_1, x_2, x_3 are statistically independent variables and a_1, a_2, a_3 are constants then (i) the mean of $(a_1x_1+a_2x_2+a_3x_3) = a_1(\text{mean of } x_1)+a_2(\text{mean of } x_2)+a_3(\text{mean of } x_3)$, and (ii) the variance of $(a_1x_1+a_2x_2+a_3x_3) = a_1^2(\text{var } x_1)+a_2^2(\text{var } x_2)+a_3^2(\text{var } x_3)$. In the example under consideration
$$a_1 = 1, \quad a_2 = 2, \quad a_3 = -1,$$
the mean of $x_1 = $ the mean of $x_2 = $ the mean of $x_3 = 3\frac{1}{2}$,
the variance of $x_1 = $ the variance of $x_2 = $ the variance of $x_3 = 2\frac{11}{12}$.
Thus the mean score $= 1\times3\frac{1}{2}+2\times3\frac{1}{2}+(-1)\times3\frac{1}{2}$
$$= 7$$
and the variance of the scores $= 1^2\times2\frac{11}{12}+2^2\times2\frac{11}{12}+(-1)^2\times2\frac{11}{12}$
$$= 17\frac{1}{2}.$$

100. Example. *A large consignment of mercury is supplied in small containers. The volumes of mercury in the containers are distributed about a mean of 250 c.c. with a standard deviation of 2 c.c. and the weights of* *the empty containers are distributed about a mean of 456 g. with a standard deviation of 7 g. Calculate the mean and standard deviation of the full containers given that the specific gravity of mercury is 13·6.*

Taking the mean of $x_1 = 250$, the mean of $x_2 = 456$,

the variance of $x_1 = 4$, the variance of $x_2 = 49$,

$$a_1 = 13\cdot6, \quad a_2 = 1$$

we obtain (i) the mean weight of the full containers is

$$13\cdot6 \times 250 + 1 \times 456 = 3856 \text{ g.}$$

and (ii) the variance of these weights is

$$13\cdot6^2 \times 4 + 1^2 \times 49 = 789 \text{ g.}^2$$

Thus the standard deviation is 28·1 g.

101. The significance of the difference between the means of two large samples. Consider the two large samples details of which are given in table 8 c.

TABLE 8C

	Sample 1	Sample 2
No. of observations	n_1	n_2
Mean	m_1	m_2
Standard deviation	s_1	s_2
Standard error	$s_1/\sqrt{n_1}$	$s_2/\sqrt{n_2}$

If we were to write down all the possible differences between the observations of sample 1 and sample 2 in the same way that we wrote down the differences of the red and black numbers in §94, the variance of the population of differences is the sum of the variances of the separate populations. Now the estimates of the variances of the separate populations are s_1^2/n_1 and s_2^2/n_2 and hence the estimated variance of the population of differences is $\dfrac{s_1^2}{n_1} + \dfrac{s_2^2}{n_2}$. Thus, *the standard error of the differences is*

$$\sqrt{\left(\frac{s_1^2}{n_1} + \frac{s_2^2}{n_2}\right)}.$$

Moreover, the mean of the differences being equal to the difference of the means is $(m_1 - m_2)$ and if sample 1 and sample 2 both belong to the same population, the mean of the differences should not differ significantly from zero. Hence, for large samples, if

$$\frac{|m_1 - m_2|}{\sqrt{\left(\dfrac{s_1^2}{n_1} + \dfrac{s_2^2}{n_2}\right)}} > 1\cdot96,$$

the difference between the means is significant at the 5 % level. This means that the chance of such a large 'difference' when the samples are from the same parent population is less than $\frac{1}{20}$.

If

$$\frac{|m_1 - m_2|}{\sqrt{\left(\dfrac{s_1^2}{n_1} + \dfrac{s_2^2}{n_2}\right)}} > 3\cdot09,$$

the difference between the means is significant at the 0·2 % level and the chance of such a large 'difference' when the samples are from the same parent population is $\frac{1}{500}$.

102. Example. *Sixty boys who entered a school A and sixty boys who entered another school B were given the same examination in English. After each group of boys had attended their respective schools for one year they were each given another common examination in English. The means and standard deviations of the marks are shown in the following table:*

Examination mark of the 60 boys in each group

| | Upon entry | | After one year in the school | |
	Mean	Standard deviation	Mean	Standard deviation
School A	53	10	51	7
School B	50	10	48	7

Show that the difference between the means was not significant at the 5 % level when the boys entered the schools but that it was significant at the 5 % level after one year.

Interpret this result. [Northern]

When the boys entered the two schools,

$$\frac{|m_1 - m_2|}{\sqrt{\left(\dfrac{s_1^2}{n_1} + \dfrac{s_2^2}{n_2}\right)}} = \frac{(53 - 50)}{\sqrt{\left(\dfrac{10^2}{60} + \dfrac{10^2}{60}\right)}}$$

$$= 1\cdot64.$$

Thus the difference between the means was not significant at the 5 % level. After one year,

$$\frac{|m_1 - m_2|}{\sqrt{\left(\dfrac{s_1^2}{n_1} + \dfrac{s_2^2}{n_2}\right)}} = \frac{(51 - 48)}{\sqrt{\left(\dfrac{7^2}{60} + \dfrac{7^2}{60}\right)}}$$

$$= 2\cdot35$$

and the difference between the means was then significant at the 5 % level. This means that when the two groups of boys entered the schools they both belonged to the same parent population. Although the mean for school A was 3 higher than that for school B the variability of the individuals was so great that the difference of 3 could be regarded as nothing more than a chance effect. The members of school A could not be considered more able to cope with the examination than those of school B. After one year, however, the two groups no longer belonged to the same parent population. The variability within the groups was reduced to such an extent that the difference of 3 could no longer be regarded as a chance effect. The tuition given in school A had been a better preparation for the examination than that given in school B.

By table A2, $A(2\cdot35) = 0\cdot99061$ which is 99 % approximately. This shows that the value, $2\cdot23$, of the s.e. is such that the two-tail probability (see §83) of the samples being from the same parent population is 2×1 %. Thus, after one year, the difference between the means is significant at the 2 % level.

103. Exercises.

1. In order to find out whether the average speed of motor-vehicles leaving London is different from that of motor-vehicles entering London, cars and motor-cycles were timed over a stretch of the Portsmouth road. The following table shows the results of the investigation:

	Leaving London	Entering London
No. of vehicles timed	50	50
Mean time in sec.	17·04	18·38
Variance in sec.^{2}	8·846	9·106

Determine whether the difference between the means is significant (i) at the 5 % level, (ii) at the 1 % level. Comment on the meaning of your result.

[Northern]

2. A firm which manufactures lead-covered submarine cable suspected that the lead was being put on more thickly by its night workers than by its day workers. To keep down the cost the lead must be as thin as possible but must be nowhere less than 0·2 in. thick if it is to withstand the action of the sea water and general wear and tear. Part of an investigation carried out is summarised in the following table:

	Day work	Night work
No. of places at which the thickness of the lead cover was measured	100	100
Mean thickness (in.)	0·292	0·298
Standard deviation (in.)	0·021	0·019

Determine whether the difference between the means is significant or not and make comments on the implications of the given figures and your result.

[Northern]

104. The significance of the difference between the means of two small samples. For small samples it is necessary to replace the expression

$$\frac{|m_1-m_2|}{\sqrt{\left(\dfrac{s_1^2}{n_1}+\dfrac{s_2^2}{n_2}\right)}} \quad \text{by} \quad \frac{|m_1-m_2|}{s\sqrt{\left(\dfrac{1}{n_1}+\dfrac{1}{n_2}\right)}},$$

where s is an estimate of the standard deviation of the parent population from which both samples are drawn. The procedure for an investigation of the difference between the means of two small samples is as follows:

(i) Assume that the two samples are drawn from the same parent population. This is the null hypothesis.

(ii) Estimate the standard deviation of this parent population by

$$s^2 = \frac{\Sigma(x_1-m_1)^2+\Sigma(x_2-m_2)^2}{(n_1-1)+(n_2-1)} \quad \text{(If the individual observations are available)}$$

or $\quad s^2 = \dfrac{(n_1-1)s_1^2+(n_2-1)s_2^2}{(n_1+n_2-2)}.\quad$ (If the standard deviations are available but not the individual observations)

Note that the number of degrees of freedom available for the calculation of s is n_1+n_2-2.

(iii) Calculate the value of

$$t = \frac{|m_1-m_2|}{s\sqrt{\left(\dfrac{1}{n_1}+\dfrac{1}{n_2}\right)}}.$$

If t is greater than the $P = 5\%$ value of the t-distribution given in table A 5 for $\nu = n_1+n_2-2$, the difference between the means is significant at the 5% level and the assumption or null hypothesis that the samples are from the same parent population must be rejected.

105. Example. *In the manufacture of insulin, the strength of the final product may be checked by making a comparison between the mean level of blood sugar in a group of rabbits inoculated with it and the mean level of blood sugar in a comparable group of rabbits inoculated with a standard preparation of known potency. The results of such a test were as follows:*
Standard preparation: 36, 61, 60, 63, 57, 58, 61, 48, 54, 75, 68, 65.
Trial preparation: 58, 58, 76, 63, 50, 54, 63, 64, 65, 87, 72, 60.
Calculate the difference between the two means and estimate its standard error. Verify that the difference is not statistically significant.
Can it be concluded that the trial and standard preparations have equal potency? Give reasons for your answer. [Northern]

Table 8D shows the calculation of

$$\Sigma x_1 = 706, \ \Sigma x_2 = 770, \ \Sigma x_1^2 = 42614 \text{ and } \Sigma x_2^2 = 50532.$$

TABLE 8D

Standard preparation x_1	Trial preparation x_2	x_1^2	x_2^2
36	58	1296	3364
61	58	3721	3364
60	76	3600	5776
63	63	3969	3969
57	50	3249	2500
58	54	3364	2916
61	63	3721	3969
48	64	2304	4096
54	65	2916	4225
75	87	5625	7569
68	72	4624	5184
65	60	4225	3600
Total 706	770	42614	50532

Thus
$$m_1 = \frac{\Sigma x_1}{n_1} \qquad\qquad m_2 = \frac{\Sigma x_2}{n_2}$$
$$= 706/12 \qquad\qquad\quad = 770/12$$
$$= 58\cdot83, \qquad\qquad\quad\ = 64\cdot17,$$

$$(n_1-1)s_1^2 = \Sigma(x_1-m_1)^2 \qquad (n_2-1)s_2^2 = \Sigma(x_2-m_2)^2$$
$$= \Sigma x_1^2 - (\Sigma x_1)^2/n_1 \qquad\qquad = \Sigma x_2^2 - (\Sigma x_2)^2/n_2$$
$$= 42614 - 706^2/12 \qquad\qquad = 50532 - 770^2/12$$
$$= 1078, \qquad\qquad\qquad\qquad = 1124.$$

Hence
$$s^2 = \frac{(n_1-1)s_1^2 + (n_2-1)s_2^2}{(n_1+n_2-2)}$$
$$= \frac{1078+1124}{22}$$
$$= 100\cdot1$$

and
$$s = 10\cdot0.$$

The estimate of the S.E. of the difference between the means is, therefore,

$$s\sqrt{\left(\frac{1}{n_1}+\frac{1}{n_2}\right)} = 10\cdot0\sqrt{\left(\frac{1}{12}+\frac{1}{12}\right)}$$
$$= 4\cdot08$$

and
$$t = \frac{|m_1-m_2|}{s\sqrt{\left(\frac{1}{n_1}+\frac{1}{n_2}\right)}}$$
$$= (64\cdot17 - 58\cdot83)/4\cdot08$$
$$= 1\cdot31.$$

Now by table A5, the $P = 5\%$ value of the t-distribution for $v = 22$ is between 2·06 and 2·09. As the calculated value of t is not greater than the $P = 5\%$ value the difference between the means is not significant and the null hypothesis is not rejected.

The null hypothesis is that both samples are drawn from the same parent population. That is to say, the trial preparation and the standard preparation are of equal potency.

106. Exercises.

1. For a random sample of 16 households from one district the sum (in shillings) of weekly rents is 190 and the sum of the squares 3059. The corresponding figures for 26 households from a second district are 340 and 6108. Estimate the mean and variance of rents in each of the two districts.

Estimate also the standard error of the difference between the two means, and test whether or not the difference is statistically significant.   [Northern]

2. Ten soldiers visit the rifle range two weeks running. The first week their scores are   67, 24, 57, 55, 63, 54, 56, 68, 33, 43.

The second week they score, in the same order,

67, 24, 57, 55, 63, 54, 56, 68, 33, 43.

70, 38, 58, 58, 56, 67, 68, 77, 42, 38.

Is there any significant improvement? How would the test be affected if the scores were not shown in the same order each time?   [A.I.S.]

3. A standard cell, whose voltage is known to be 1·10 volts, was used to test the accuracy of two voltmeters, A and B. Ten independent readings of the voltage of the cell were taken with each voltmeter, and the results were as follows:

| A | 1·11 | 1·15 | 1·14 | 1·10 | 1·09 | 1·11 | 1·12 | 1·15 | 1·13 | 1·14 |
| B | 1·12 | 1·06 | 1·02 | 1·08 | 1·11 | 1·05 | 1·06 | 1·03 | 1·05 | 1·08 |

From these results is there any evidence of bias in either voltmeter?
[R.S.S.]

4. A group of 7 seven-week-old chickens, reared on a high-protein diet, weigh 12, 15, 11, 16, 14, 14, 16 ounces; a second group of 5 chickens, similarly treated except that they receive a low-protein diet, weigh 8, 10, 14, 10, 13 ounces.

Calculate the value of t and test whether there is significant evidence that additional protein has increased the weight of the chickens. Criticize the arrangement of the experiment and suggest improvements in design.
[R.S.S.]

5. A group of 8 psychology students were tested for their ability to remember certain material, and their scores (number of items remembered) were as follows:

A	B	C	D	E	F	G	H
19	14	13	16	19	18	16	17

They were then given special training purporting to improve memory and were re-tested after a month.

Their scores were then:

A	B	C	D	E	F	G	H
26	20	17	21	23	24	21	18

A control group of 7 students was also tested and re-tested after a month, but was not given special training. The scores in the two tests were:

J	K	L	M	N	O	P
21	19	16	22	18	20	19
21	23	16	24	17	17	16

Compare the change in each of the two groups by calculating t and test whether there is significant evidence to show the value of the special training. Is there evidence that the experiment was not properly designed?

[R.S.S.]

6. Sickness rates for two factories over a period of 6 months were as follows:

Rate per 100

	Factory A	Factory B
January	64	75
February	72	83
March	79	74
April	58	67
May	49	52
June	40	46

By means of the t-test, or otherwise, examine whether there is any significant difference between the two factories. [A.I.S.]

7. From each of two batches of electric lamps made by the same manufacturer, a random sample of six was chosen and tested by burning out. The results were as follows:

Lamp no.	1	2	3	4	5	6
Length of ⌠Batch A	802	959	1022	1040	733	897
life (hr.) ⌡Batch B	839	961	1035	896	994	950

Is there any significant difference in average length of life between the two batches?

The average length of life should be at least 1000 hr. to satisfy a certain specification. Is there any reason to suppose, from the given data, that the manufacturer's product is not likely to meet this specification? [R.S.S.]

9

Quality Control

107. Control of a given dimension. When articles are being mass produced some variation in the dimensions must be expected and a certain tolerance limit is allowed in their specification. Thus, a dimension stated as 1.005 ± 0.005 in. has tolerance limits of 1.00 and 1.01 in. It is often possible, by random sampling, to ensure that the total output is within the tolerance limits. This application of statistics to industrial and manufacturing processes is known as *quality control*. Quality control is concerned with the collection, analysis and presentation of facts concerning quality. The quality control of a given dimension is a direct application of the normal distribution.

108. Control of the fraction defective. A second type of quality control is an application of the Poisson distribution. It is used when the articles being manufactured are not classified by dimensions but are deemed either *sound* or *defective* (*acceptable* or *unacceptable*) according as they either pass or fail a certain test of quality.

109. The value of random sampling. The method of judging the quality of the whole output by a system of random sampling is important not only because *it saves time and money*, but also because *the sample tested is often completely destroyed* in the test. The quality of the whole output of a munitions factory, for example, is tested by actually exploding random samples of its products.

TABLE 9A

Conversion of range to standard deviation (Reproduced from Lindley and Miller, *Cambridge Elementary Statistical Tables*, page 7)

n	a_n	n	a_n	n	a_n	n	a_n
2	0·8862	5	0·4299	8	0·3512	11	0·3152
3	0·5908	6	0·3946	9	0·3367	12	0·3069
4	0·4857	7	0·3698	10	0·3249	13	0·2998

An estimate of the standard deviation is given by multiplying the mean range of random samples of size n, from a normal population, by a_n. The mean range in samples of size n from a normal population is the standard deviation of the population divided by a_n.

110. The estimation of the standard deviation from the mean range of samples of n observations. In industrial quality control, the standard deviation is not usually *calculated* from the sums of squares. Instead it is *estimated* by table 9A from the ranges of samples as shown in the following example.

111. Example. *Consider the 5 samples, each of 4 observations, given in §82 for which the calculated mean and standard deviation were found to be 1·0055 in. and 0·00322 in. respectively. Rewritten in thousandths of an inch above 1·000, the observations are as given in table 9B:*

TABLE 9B

Sample no. ...	1	2	3	4	5
	10	2	9	5	6
	2	7	7	11	2
	7	8	3	2	1
	7	5	0	8	8
Sample mean	$6\frac{1}{2}$	$5\frac{1}{2}$	$4\frac{3}{4}$	$6\frac{1}{2}$	$4\frac{1}{4}$
Range	8	6	9	9	7

The mean of the sample means is

$$\tfrac{1}{5}(6\tfrac{1}{2}+5\tfrac{1}{2}+4\tfrac{3}{4}+6\tfrac{1}{2}+4\tfrac{1}{4}) = 5\text{·}5 \text{ thousandths above } 1\text{·}000$$
$$= 1\text{·}0055 \text{ in.}$$

The mean range is

$$\tfrac{1}{5}(8+6+9+9+7) = 7\text{·}8 \text{ thousandths.}$$

By table 9A, $a_4 = 0\text{·}4857$ and the estimated standard deviation is

$$7\text{·}8 \times 0\text{·}4857 = 3\text{·}787 \text{ thousandths}$$
$$= 0\text{·}0038 \text{ in.}$$

112. A quality-control chart for means. Quality control of a given dimension is maintained by two charts, one showing the means of successive samples and the other their ranges (or standard deviations). In §85 we learned that, if the estimated standard deviation of the individual observations is σ, the estimated standard deviation of the means of samples of size n is $\sigma/\sqrt{n}$. Moreover, even though the individual observations are not normally distributed, it is likely that the means of samples are fairly normally distributed. Thus

(i) the probability of a sample having a mean outside the limits

$$\text{mean} \pm \frac{1\text{·}96\sigma}{\sqrt{n}} \quad \text{(the 95 \% zone)}$$

is 1 in 20,

83

(ii) the probability of a sample having a mean outside the limits

$$\text{mean} \pm \frac{3\cdot09\sigma}{\sqrt{n}} \quad \text{(the 99·8 \% zone)}$$

is 1 in 500.

In the example of the last paragraph

(i) the 95 % zone is $1\cdot0055 \pm 1\cdot96 \times 0\cdot0038/\sqrt{4} = 1\cdot0055 \pm 0\cdot0037$,
i.e. between $1\cdot002$ and $1\cdot009$ (to the nearest thousandth);

(ii) the 99·8 % zone is $1\cdot0055 \pm 3\cdot09 \times 0\cdot0038/\sqrt{4} = 1\cdot0055 \pm 0\cdot0059$,
i.e. between $1\cdot000$ and $1\cdot011$ (to the nearest thousandth).

The quality-control chart for means in this case is shown in fig. 10. It is a graph with a pair of horizontal lines, $\bar{x} = 1\cdot002$ and $\bar{x} = 1\cdot009$, called the *inner control* lines and another pair, $\bar{x} = 1\cdot000$ and $\bar{x} = 1\cdot011$, called the *outer control* lines. If the mean of each random sample of 4 observations is plotted on this chart and only 1 mean out of every 20 falls outside the inner control limits (and only 1 out of every 500 outside the outer control limits) *the production is said to be under control.* Immediately these proportions are exceeded *the production is out of control.*

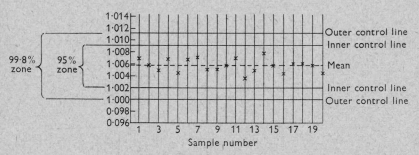

Fig. 10. A quality-control chart for means.

In the example given, the estimates of the mean and the standard deviation were based on 5 samples only. This may be necessary if it is desired to get a system of control operating as quickly as possible, but it is advisable to make a second estimate of the mean and the standard deviation when another 10 or 20 samples are available and to readjust the control lines accordingly.

In fig. 10 the means of the 5 samples given in §111 have been plotted and also the means of the next 15 samples given in table 9c.

Figure 8 indicates that production was under control over the whole period during which the 20 samples were drawn.

TABLE 9C

Sample no. ...	6	7	8	9	10	11	12	13
Sample mean	$6\frac{1}{2}$	$6\frac{3}{4}$	5	5	$5\frac{1}{2}$	$6\frac{3}{4}$	$3\frac{1}{2}$	$5\frac{1}{4}$
Range	8	9	6	8	7	9	7	8

Sample no. ...	14	15	16	17	18	19	20
Sample mean	$7\frac{1}{2}$	$5\frac{1}{2}$	$4\frac{1}{4}$	$5\frac{3}{4}$	$5\frac{3}{4}$	$5\frac{1}{2}$	$4\frac{1}{2}$
Range	5	9	6	8	8	9	7

113. Exercise.

*Mass-produced 100-ohm electrical resistors. Random samples of
5 resistors drawn during the course of production
(resistances given in ohms above 90)*

Sample no. ...	1	2	3	4	5	6	7	8	9	10
Beginning of	9	8	14	13	9	11	5	7	9	10
production	8	15	12	5	13	11	12	10	12	10
	6	15	14	12	8	9	12	8	10	12
	8	14	12	5	14	16	9	10	10	13
	13	11	13	11	9	14	15	9	15	13

Sample no. ...	11	12	13	14	15	16	17	18	19	20
After 1 week	17	6	9	17	11	14	6	12	10	11
	17	13	9	7	13	14	9	7	4	12
	10	14	9	9	7	9	10	12	10	11
	8	13	16	10	7	13	14	15	11	7
	6	13	11	18	13	12	12	11	9	15

Sample no. ...	21	22	23	24	25	26	27	28	29	30
After 4 weeks	12	12	15	10	14	8	3	15	11	15
	7	17	10	14	8	4	11	7	18	9
	14	13	13	17	3	16	11	1	15	10
	14	10	13	19	17	10	16	16	11	7
	9	10	15	17	16	15	8	15	11	12

Random samples nos. 1–10 above were drawn soon after production had
begun, samples nos. 11–20 about 1 week later and samples nos. 21–30 about
4 weeks later. Use the first 10 samples to set up a quality-control chart for
means by calculating

(i) the mean of the sample means,
(ii) the mean range,
(iii) the 95 % zone,
(iv) the 99·8 % zone.

Plot the means of samples nos. 11–20 on the chart and comment on the
quality of production after 1 week.

Plot the means of samples nos. 21–30 on the chart and comment on the
quality of production after 4 weeks.

114. A quality-control chart for ranges.
By using table 9B a quality-
control chart for ranges can be set up to ensure that variation within

the samples is not too great. Thus for the 5 samples of §111 we take the estimate of σ, 3·787 thousandths, and obtain

(i) the 97·5 % zone for ranges,

$$D_{0\cdot975} \times \sigma = 3\cdot98 \times 3\cdot787$$

$$= 15\cdot1 \text{ thousandths,}$$

(ii) the 99·9 % zone for ranges,

$$D_{0\cdot999} \times \sigma = 5\cdot30 \times 3\cdot787$$

$$= 20\cdot1 \text{ thousandths.}$$

TABLE 9D

Distribution of ranges of samples

n	2	3	4	5	6	7	8	9	10	11	12
$D_{0\cdot975}$	3·17	3·68	3·98	4·20	4·36	4·49	4·61	4·70	4·79	4·86	4·92
$D_{0\cdot999}$	4·65	5·05	5·30	5·45	5·60	5·70	5·80	5·90	5·95	6·05	6·10

If σ is the standard deviation of the population of individual observations (i) 97·5 % of the ranges of samples of size n will not exceed $D_{0\cdot975} \times \sigma$, (ii) 99·9 % of the ranges of samples of size n will not exceed $D_{0\cdot999} \times \sigma$.

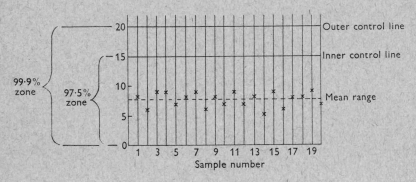

Fig. 11. A quality-control chart for ranges.

Figure 11 shows the quality-control chart. On it are plotted the ranges of samples nos. 1–5 given in §111 followed by samples nos. 6–20 given in §112. If only 1 range out of every 40 is above the inner control limit (or only 1 out of every 1000 above the outer control limit) the production is under control. If these proportions are exceeded the production is out of control. Figure 11 shows that for the example under consideration quality is being well maintained.

86

115. Exercise.

Using the first ten samples of §113, set up a quality-control chart for ranges. Plot the ranges of samples nos. 11–20 on the chart and comment on production after 1 week.

Plot the ranges of samples nos. 21–30 on the chart and comment on production after 4 weeks.

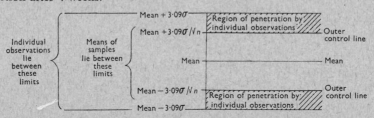

Fig. 12. The shaded regions of width $(3 \cdot 09\sigma - 3 \cdot 09\sigma/\sqrt{n})$ are the regions into which individual observations may penetrate even though the means of samples lie between the outer control lines. (We assume here that the practical 100 % zone of a normal distribution is $3 \cdot 09$ either side of the mean.)

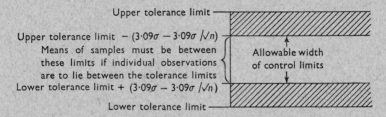

Fig. 13. The allowable width of control limits if the articles produced are to be within the specified tolerance limits.

116. Allowable width of control limits when tolerance limits are specified.

When tolerance limits are specified it is necessary to ensure that the articles produced are within the tolerance requirements. Figure 12 illustrates the fact that even when the means of samples are between the outer control lines the individual observations may penetrate into a region of width $(3 \cdot 09\sigma - 3 \cdot 09\sigma/\sqrt{n})$ outside the control lines. In fig. 13 this region has been transferred from fig. 12 and placed inside the tolerance limits to give the *allowable width of control limits* within which the means of samples must lie if the individual observations are to be between the tolerance limits.

In the example of §111 let us suppose that the tolerance limits are 0·095 to 1·015. Since $\sigma = 3 \cdot 787$ thousandths

$$(3 \cdot 09\sigma - 3 \cdot 09\sigma/\sqrt{n}) = 5 \cdot 85 \text{ thousandths}$$

$$= 0 \cdot 006 \text{ in. (to the nearest thousandth),}$$

and the allowable width of the control limits is

$$0.095 + 0.006 \quad \text{to} \quad 1.015 - 0.006,$$

i.e. $\qquad\qquad\qquad 1.001 \quad \text{to} \quad 1.009.$

As the means of all 20 samples lie within these limits we conclude that the compression springs produced during the period covered by the sample are within the tolerance requirements.

117. Exercise.

Given that the tolerance limits of the 100-ohm electrical resistors of §113 are 100 ± 9 ohms establish allowable width of control limits based on the first 10 samples and determine whether or not production was to tolerance requirements (i) after one week, (ii) after four weeks.

118. Control chart for fraction defective.

It was mentioned in §108 that when articles being manufactured are not classified by dimensions, but are deemed either sound or defective, the quality of production is controlled by an application of the Poisson distribution. It is usually necessary for this type of control to sample at least 20 % of the output. When 20 or more samples have been examined it is possible to set up a control chart which indicates that *production is under control provided not more than one point in ten lies above the control line.* The following example illustrates the method:

A random sample of 20 articles was drawn from every 100 produced by a certain process. The number of defectives per sample in the first 20 samples were

$$0, 1, 0, 1, 1, 3, 0, 2, 1, 0, 0, 0, 0, 3, 0, 0, 2, 1, 1, 2;$$

and in the second 20 samples were

$$1, 2, 2, 0, 1, 2, 0, 1, 2, 2, 0, 1, 0, 0, 1, 0, 1, 1, 1, 1.$$

Use the first 20 samples to calculate the mean number of defectives per sample and by using the Poisson distribution obtain a CONTROL LIMIT *c such that the probability of there being c or more defectives in a sample is less than* $\frac{1}{10}$.

Use c to set up a control chart and show that over the whole period during which the samples were drawn the process was under control with a process mean of $4\frac{1}{2}$ % *defective.*

As there were 18 defectives in the first 20 samples the mean number of defectives per sample is 0·9.

By substituting $a = 0.9$ in the Poisson distribution

$$e^{-a}, \quad ae^{-a}, \quad \frac{a^2}{2!}e^{-a}, \quad \frac{a^3}{3!}e^{-a}, \quad \dots$$

we find the probabilities of $0, 1, 2, 3, \dots$ defectives per sample are

$$0.4066, \quad 0.3659, \quad 0.1647, \quad 0.0494, \quad \dots.$$

It is now necessary to decide how many of these probabilities must be added together to make a total greater than $\frac{9}{10}$. As the sum of the first three probabilities is 0.9372 the probability of 3 *or more* defectives per sample is less than $\frac{1}{10}$. Thus the required CONTROL LIMIT $c = 3$.

A control chart can now be set up as shown in fig. 14. As no points fall above the control limit (and only 2 out of 40 fall on it) the process is under control. In the first 20 samples, there are 18 defectives out of a total of 400. This establishes the process mean as $4\frac{1}{2}\%$ and the process is stated to be under control with a process average of $4\frac{1}{2}\%$ defective.

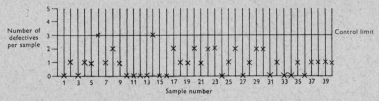

Fig. 14. Quality-control chart for fraction defective. If more than 1 point out of 10 falls above the control limit, the process is out of control.

It may be noted that, on the average, there were 9 defectives in every 200 articles tested and when discovered these would be rejected. However, for every 9 defectives discovered and rejected there were 36 undiscovered, because for every 200 articles tested 800 passed by untested. Thus there were finally about 36 defectives remaining in every 991 produced. The application of quality control, therefore, caused the reduction of the process average from $4\frac{1}{2}\%$ defective to 3.6% defective.

In this chapter only a very brief outline of the methods of quality control has been given, but it is sufficient to show how a chart can be used to indicate the overall position of a manufacturing process. It shows up the good results as well as the bad ones. It shows that variability in production, although unavoidable, can be acceptable.

119. Exercise.

A random sample of 20 articles was drawn from every 100 produced by a certain process. The number of defectives per sample in the first 20 samples were

0, 2, 0, 1, 1, 2, 1, 4, 2, 1, 3, 1, 3, 1, 1, 0, 3, 1, 1, 2

and in the second 20 samples were

$$1, 1, 2, 1, 2, 1, 1, 2, 1, 2, 3, 3, 0, 0, 5, 5, 2, 3, 3, 3.$$

Use the first 20 samples to calculate the mean number of defectives per sample and then, by the Poisson distribution, obtain the CONTROL LIMIT c such that the probability of there being c or more defectives per sample is less than $\frac{1}{10}$.

Set up a control chart and determine whether or not the process was under control during the whole period.

10

Method of Least Squares

120. A bivariate distribution. Table 10 A shows, side by side, the number of vehicles, x, on the roads of Great Britain and the total casualties, y, in road accidents for the years 1945–54. The source is the *Annual Abstract of Statistics.*

TABLE IOA

	Vehicles with licences current during the September quarter (millions)	Total casualties in road accidents (thousands)
	x	y
1945	2·6	138
1946	3·1	163
1947	3·5	166
1948	3·7	153
1949	4·1	177
1950	4·4	201
1951	4·6	216
1952	4·9	208
1953	5·3	226
1954	5·8	238

The number of vehicles is seen to have steadily increased, and the number of road accidents has also increased though not quite so regularly. The ten (x,y) pairs of values are an example of a *bivariate distribution.*

121. The scatter diagram: direct correlation. If the value x is plotted on a graph against its corresponding value y as shown in fig. 15, a *scatter diagram* is obtained.

Although the points on the scatter diagram do not fall exactly along a straight line they fall within quite a narrow belt. Small values of y correspond to small values of x, large values of y to large values of x, and x and y are said to be *directly correlated.* The exercises at the end of this chapter will provide the student with further examples of *direct correlation.*

122. Inverse correlation. In the bivariate distribution of x and y shown in table 10 B, *small* values of y correspond to *large* values of x and

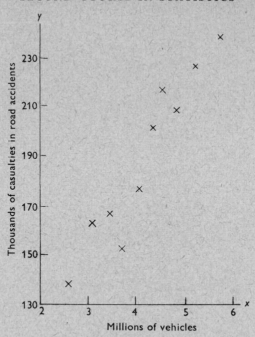

Fig. 15. Scatter diagram showing direct correlation.

TABLE IOB

Cinema admissions and television licences issued

Year and quarter		Towns served by Sutton Coldfield TV transmitter		Towns not normally served by any TV transmitter	
		Cinema admissions (millions) x	TV licences (per 1000 population) y	Cinema admissions (millions) z	TV licences (per 1000 population)
1950	1	11·0	12	12·1	—
	2	10·0	18	11·2	—
	3	10·0	24	11·6	—
	4	9·4	37	10·6	—
1951	1	10·5	52	12·1	—
	2	9·7	64	11·8	—
	3	9·4	69	11·5	—
	4	9·3	81	10·9	1
1952	1	9·9	98	11·6	2
	2	9·3	101	11·1	3
	3	9·0	106	11·3	3
	4	8·6	119	10·5	4

[Northern]

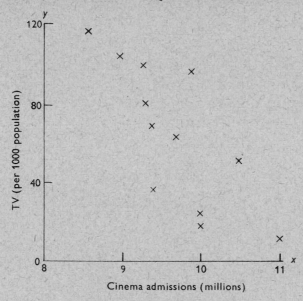

Fig. 16. Scatter diagram showing inverse correlations.

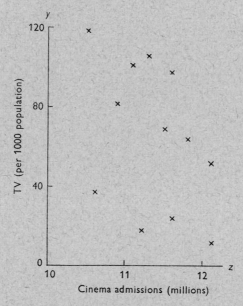

Fig. 17. Scatter diagram of a bivariate distribution in which
the variables are not correlated.

93

vice versa. This is known as *inverse correlation*. In the scatter diagram (fig. 16) the points lie within a fairly well-defined belt which is downward sloping for increasing values of x.

123. Absence of correlation. Figure 17 is the scatter diagram of the bivariate distribution of y and z of table 10B. One would not expect correlation in this case because it is unlikely that the *cinema admissions* in one group of towns should be related to the *number of TV licences* issued in a completely different group of towns. This is confirmed by the scatter diagram, the points of which do not lie within any well-defined belt.

124. How to calculate the equation of the least squares line of regression of y on x. Figure 18 shows the scatter diagram of fig. 15 with a straight line fitted through the middle of the ten points. The straight line in this case is *the least squares line of regression of y on x*. It indicates how the

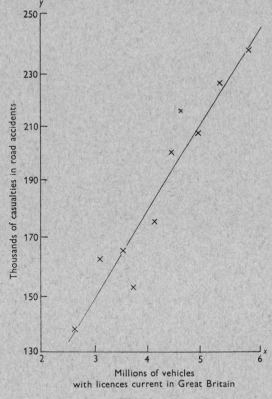

Fig. 18

94

thousands of casualties, y, in any year *depend* on the *millions of vehicles*, x, on the roads in that year. In this case x is the *independent variable* and y the *dependent variable*.

The equation of the least squares line of regression of y on x for the n points (x_1, y_1), (x_2, y_2), ... (x_n, y_n) is calculated by first supposing that it is of the form

$$y = ax + b,$$

where a and b are constants. The values of a and b are then found by solving the two simultaneous equations

$$\Sigma y = a\Sigma x + nb, \tag{1}$$

$$\Sigma xy = a\Sigma x^2 + b\Sigma x, \tag{2}$$

where $\quad \Sigma x = x_1 + x_2 + \dots + x_n, \qquad \Sigma y = y_1 + y_2 + \dots + y_n,$

$\quad \Sigma x^2 = x_1^2 + x_2^2 + \dots + x_n^2, \qquad \Sigma xy = x_1 y_1 + x_2 y_2 + \dots + x_n y_n.$

The equations (1) and (2) above are called the *normal equations*. Their formal derivation is given in §125. Note that equation (1) is obtained from $y = ax + b$ by placing Σ before y and x and n before b, and equation (2) is obtained by first multiplying $y = ax + b$ by x and then placing Σ before xy, x^2 and x. The actual calculation of the equation of the straight line shown in fig. 18 is given in table 10 c.

TABLE 10C

Calculation of the equation of the least squares line of regression of y on x

x	y	x^2	xy
2·6	138	6·76	358·8
3·1	163	9·61	505·3
3·5	166	12·25	581·0
3·7	153	13·69	566·1
4·1	177	16·81	725·7
4·4	201	19·36	884·4
4·6	216	21·16	993·6
4·9	208	24·01	1019·2
5·3	226	28·09	1197·8
5·8	238	33·64	1380·4

$\Sigma x = 42\cdot0 \quad \Sigma y = 1886 \quad \Sigma x^2 = 185\cdot38 \quad \Sigma xy = 8212\cdot3$

The constants a and b of the straight line $y = ax + b$ are given by the equations

$$1886 = 42\cdot0a + 10b,$$

$$8212\cdot3 = 185\cdot38a + 42\cdot0b.$$

Thus $a = 32$, $b = 53$ and the equation of the least squares line of regression of y on x is

$$y = 32x + 53.$$

125. The formal derivation of the normal equations. Suppose that $P_1, P_2, \dots, P_n$ are n points whose co-ordinates are

$$(x_1, y_1), (x_2, y_2), \dots (x_n, y_n)$$

respectively and that AB is a straight line whose equation is $y = ax + b$ (see fig. 19). The ordinates $P_1 R_1, P_2 R_2, \dots, P_n R_n$ have respective lengths $y_1, y_2, \dots, y_n$ and if $Q_1, Q_2, \dots, Q_n$ are the respective points of intersection of the ordinates with the line AB then $Q_1 R_1, Q_2 R_2, \dots, Q_n R_n$ have respective lengths $(ax_1 + b), (ax_2 + b), \dots, (ax_n + b)$. Thus the *residuals* $P_1 Q_1, P_2 Q_2, \dots, P_n Q_n$ have respective lengths

$$(y_1 - ax_1 - b), (y_2 - ax_2 - b), \dots, (y_n - ax_n - b),$$

and if z represents the sum of the squares of the lengths of the residuals

$$z = (y_1 - ax_1 - b)^2 + (y_2 - ax_2 - b)^2 + \dots + (y_n - ax_n - b)^2.$$

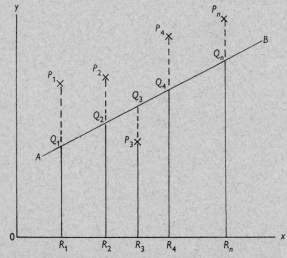

Fig. 19. The least squares line of regression of y on x is such that the sum of the squares of the residuals $P_1 Q_1^2 + P_2 Q_2^2 + \dots + P_n Q_n^2$ is a minimum.

By varying the constants a and b the position of the line AB can be altered. If b varies while a remains constant the line takes up a series of positions keeping a constant direction. If a varies while b remains constant the line rotates about a fixed point on the y-axis.

The least squares line of regression of y on x is the line whose position is chosen so that z is a minimum. Differentiating z with respect to b and regarding a as constant we obtain

$$\frac{\partial z}{\partial b} = -2(y_1 - ax_1 - b) - 2(y_2 - ax_2 - b) - \dots - 2(y_n - ax_n - b),$$

and differentiating z with respect to a and regarding b as constant we obtain

$$\frac{\partial z}{\partial a} = -2x_1(y_1 - ax_1 - b) - 2x_2(y_2 - ax_2 - b) - \ldots - 2x_n(y_n - ax_n - b).$$

If z is a minimum $\qquad \dfrac{\partial z}{\partial b} = 0 \quad$ and $\quad \dfrac{\partial z}{\partial a} = 0.$

Thus $\qquad (y_1 - ax_1 - b) + (y_2 - ax_2 - b) + \ldots + (y_n - ax_n - b) = 0$

and

$$x_1(y_1 - ax_1 - b) + x_2(y_2 - ax_2 - b) + \ldots + x_n(y_n - ax_n - b) = 0.$$

Using the Σ notation these equations can be expressed as

$$\Sigma y - a\Sigma x - nb = 0$$

and $\qquad\qquad \Sigma xy - a\Sigma x^2 - b\Sigma x = 0.$

Thus, if $y = ax + b$ is the equation of the least squares line of regression of y on x, the values of a and b are given by the normal equations

$$\Sigma y = a\Sigma x + nb,$$

$$\Sigma xy = a\Sigma x^2 + b\Sigma x.$$

126. The regression line passes through the mean of the array. The first of the normal equations $\Sigma y = a\Sigma x + nb$ can be written in the form

$$\frac{\Sigma y}{n} = a\frac{\Sigma x}{n} + b,$$

or $\qquad\qquad\qquad \bar{y} = a\bar{x} + b,$

where $\bar{y}$ represents the mean of the n values of y and $\bar{x}$ represents the mean of the n values of x. Thus the co-ordinates $(\bar{x}, \bar{y})$ of the point known as the mean of the array of points $(x_1, y_1), (x_2, y_2), \ldots, (x_n, y_n)$ satisfy the equation $y = ax + b$. This implies that the regression line passes through the mean of the array. This property was used in my *First Course in Statistics* to fix the position of the regression line.

Reference to table 10 C shows that the mean of the array of points in fig. 18 is $(4 \cdot 2, 188 \cdot 6)$ and the regression line will be observed to pass through it.

127. The regression coefficient. The constant a which is the slope of the regression line is known as the *coefficient of regression of y on x*. Table 10 C indicates that the regression coefficient of that particular example is 44 thousand casualties per million vehicles.

The student will find it an easy exercise to deduce from the normal equations that the general value of a is given by

$$a = \frac{n\Sigma xy - \Sigma x \Sigma y}{n\Sigma x^2 - (\Sigma x)^2}$$

$$= \frac{\dfrac{\Sigma xy}{n} - \left(\dfrac{\Sigma x}{n}\right)\left(\dfrac{\Sigma y}{n}\right)}{\dfrac{\Sigma x^2}{n} - \left(\dfrac{\Sigma x}{n}\right)^2}.$$

Now the *variance* of $x_1, x_2, ..., x_n$ is defined as

$$s_x^2 = \frac{\Sigma(x-\bar{x})^2}{n}$$

$$= \frac{\Sigma x^2 - 2\bar{x}\Sigma x + n\bar{x}^2}{n}$$

$$= \frac{\Sigma x^2}{n} - \left(\frac{\Sigma x}{n}\right)^2$$

and the *covariance* of $(x_1, y_1), (x_2, y_2), ..., (x_n, y_n)$ is defined as

$$s_{xy} = \frac{\Sigma(x-\bar{x})(y-\bar{y})}{n}$$

$$= \frac{\Sigma xy - \bar{x}\Sigma y - \bar{y}\Sigma x + n\bar{x}\bar{y}}{n}$$

$$= \frac{\Sigma xy}{n} - \left(\frac{\Sigma x}{u}\right)\left(\frac{\Sigma y}{n}\right).$$

Thus the coefficient of regression $a = s_{xy}/s_x^2$ and since the regression line passes through $(\bar{x}, \bar{y})$ an alternative form of its equation is

$$(y-\bar{y}) = \frac{s_{xy}}{s_x^2}(x-\bar{x}).$$

128. The line of regression of x on y. If values of x are to be estimated from known values of y the line of regression of x on y is used. This line has an equation
$$x = a'y + b',$$

where a and b are found from the normal equations

$$\Sigma x = a'\Sigma y + nb'$$

and
$$\Sigma xy = a'\Sigma y^2 + b'\Sigma y.$$

The value of a' in this case is the *coefficient of regression of x on y*. By interchanging x and y in §126 we find that

$$a' = \frac{n\Sigma xy - \Sigma x\Sigma y}{n\Sigma y^2 - (\Sigma y)^2}$$

$$= \frac{S_{xy}}{S_y^2}$$

and an alternative form of the equation of the line of regression of x on y is

$$(x - \bar{x}) = \frac{S_{xy}}{S_y^2}(y - \bar{y}).$$

This is the case in which y is the *independent variable* and x the *dependent variable*. The line of regression of x on y is illustrated by fig. 20 in which the residuals are parallel to the x-axis.

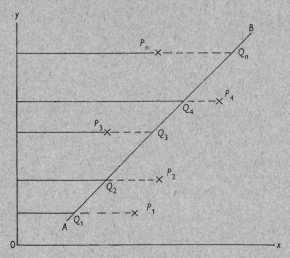

Fig. 20. The least squares line of regression of x on y, represented by AB above, is such that the sum of the squares of the residuals

$$P_1Q_1^2 + P_2Q_2^2 + \ldots + P_nQ_n^2 = (x_1 - a'y_1 - b')^2 + (x_2 - a'y_2 - b')^2 + \ldots + (x_n - a'y_n - b')^2$$

is a minimum.

129. The two lines of regression in one diagram. Figure 21 is an enlargement of fig. 16 with the two regression lines fitted. AB is the line of regression of x on y, while CD is the line of regression of y on x. AB is used to estimate the cinema admissions for a given number of TV licences per 1000 population. CD would be used to estimate the TV licences per 1000 population for a given number of cinema admissions.

As the effect of the new form of entertainment on the old is of greater interest than the effect of the old on the new, AB is of greater use than CD.

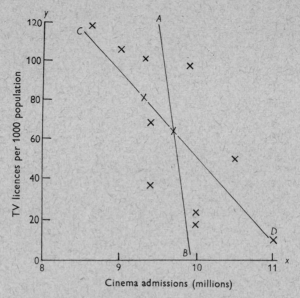

Fig. 21. AB is the line of regression of x on y. CD is the line of regression of y on x. In this example AB is of greater interest than CD.

130. Exercises.

1. The following table gives the percentage of sand in soil at different depths:

										Total
x (depth in in.)	0	6	12	18	24	30	36	42	48	216
y (% sand)	80·6	63·0	64·3	62·5	57·5	59·2	40·8	46·9	37·6	512·4

and the following sums of squares and products were calculated from the above data:

$$\Sigma(x-\bar{x})^2 = 2160\cdot00,$$

$$\Sigma(x-\bar{x})(y-\bar{y}) = -1623\cdot60,$$

$$\Sigma(y-\bar{y})^2 = 1422\cdot36.$$

Find (giving the numbers correct to three significant figures) the equations of the regression lines which you would use (i) to predict the depth from the percentage sand, (ii) to estimate the dependence of percentage of sand on depth.

Show these lines (labelled (i) and (ii)) on a scatter diagram of the original data. [London]

2. *Percentage shrinkage in samples of cloth after washing,*
in directions along and across the cloth

Along (x)	Across (y)	Along (x)	Across (y)
12	5	7	5
4	2	12	7
10	5	18	10
10	8	14	7
11	6	14	8
10	8	8	4
6	3	11	6
6	4	17	8
6	3	21	11
13	5	12	9

Calculate the equation of the line of regression of x on y.

A roll of cloth is sampled by cutting a narrow test strip right across the roll. The strip proves to have a percentage shrinkage of 7. Use your regression equation to obtain an estimate of the percentage shrinkage to be expected along the cloth.

It is desired to cut from the roll a piece of cloth which may be expected to shrink to 10 in. square after washing. Describe how this piece should be cut.

[Northern]

3. Five groups of locusts, each containing 120, were exposed to a lethal spray in various concentrations. The deaths resulting were as follows:

Concentration (multiple of standard)	1·2	1·4	1·6	1·8	2·0
No. of deaths	38	52	46	76	66

For each concentration, find the percentage of locusts dying. Plot this percentage against the concentration on a scatter diagram and calculate the equation of the line of regression, taking concentration as your independent variable.

[Northern]

4. To find the electrical resistance r of a wire, it was connected in a Wheatstone bridge circuit and the following series of readings were made:

x	0·1	0·2	0·3	0·4	0·5	0·6	0·7	0·8	0·9	1·0
y	0·270	0·476	0·702	0·910	1·106	1·350	1·560	1·742	1·994	2·182

Assuming that errors occur in the values of y but not in the values of x and that x and y satisfy the equation $y = rx + R$ where R is the resistance of the rest of the circuit, find the best values of r and R.

5. The number of grams of a given salt which will dissolve in 100 g. of water at different temperatures is shown in the table below:

Temperature ($x°$ C.)	0	10	20	30	40	50	60	70	80	90	100
Weight of salt (y g.)	53·5	59·5	65·2	70·6	75·5	80·2	85·5	90·0	95·0	99·2	104·0

Use the method of least squares to find the linear formula $y = a + bx$ which best fits these observations.

[London]

6. A general knowledge test consisting of a hundred questions was given to fifteen boys of different ages with results as follows:

Boy	Age Years	Months	No. of questions correct
A	11	7	18
B	11	1	19
C	12	8	23
D	12	0	26
E	13	5	25
F	13	6	31
G	14	9	24
H	15	3	32
I	14	7	28
J	15	6	25
K	15	9	33
L	15	7	31
M	16	11	36
N	17	1	32
O	16	10	40

Plot a scatter diagram of the numbers of questions correct (y) against the age in months (x), using 1 in. to represent 10 correct questions on the y-axis and 1 in. to represent 10 months on the x-axis. Calculate the equation of the line of regression of y on x and show the line on the diagram.

State, with reasons, which boy deserves the prize for the best performance taking age into consideration. [Northern]

7. To fit a parabola $y = ax^2 + bx + c$ to data by the method of least squares we find the values of a, b, c that will make z a minimum where

$$z = (y_1 - ax_1^2 - bx_1 - c)^2 + (y_2 - ax_2^2 - bx_2 - c)^2 + \ldots + (y_n - ax_n^2 - bx_n - c)^2.$$

By letting $\dfrac{\partial z}{\partial c} = 0, \dfrac{\partial z}{\partial b} = 0$ and $\dfrac{\partial z}{\partial a} = 0$ show that the *normal* equations are

$$\Sigma y = a\Sigma x^2 + b\Sigma x + nc,$$
$$\Sigma xy = a\Sigma x^3 + b\Sigma x^2 + c\Sigma x,$$
$$\Sigma x^2 y = a\Sigma x^4 + b\Sigma x^3 + c\Sigma x^2.$$

8. *Result of fertiliser experiment on crop results*

Units of fertiliser used	0	2	4	6	8	10
Units of yield	110	113	118	119	120	118

Fit a parabola (see Ex. 7 above) to the above data, and estimate for what fertiliser application the best results are obtained. [London]

11

Correlation by Product-Moments

131. The coefficient of correlation r_{xy}. An elementary treatment of the coefficient of correlation was given in my *First Course in Statistics*. The following introduction is more formal.

The line of regression of y on x was established in §127 as

$$(y-\bar{y}) = \frac{s_{xy}}{s_x^2}(x-\bar{x}).$$

If this equation is *standardized* by putting it in the form

$$\frac{(y-\bar{y})}{s_y} = \frac{s_{xy}}{s_x s_y}\frac{(x-\bar{x})}{s_x}$$

it can be written $$Y = r_{xy}X,$$

where the symbol r_{xy} represents $s_{xy}/s_x s_y$ and the axes of X and Y have their origin at the mean of the array, the X-axis being graduated in units equal to s_x and the Y-axis in units equal to s_y.

Similarly the line of regression of X on Y can be put in the form $X = r_{xy}Y$.

The two lines of regression referred to their new axes will then appear as shown in fig. 22. It will be seen that $Y = r_{xy}X$ makes an angle θ with the X-axis where $\tan\theta = r_{xy}$ and $X = r_{xy}Y$ makes the same angle θ with the Y-axis.

If the correlation is direct and the points of the scatter diagram lie exactly along a straight line, the two lines of regression coincide, θ is $45°$ and $r_{xy} = 1$.

If the correlation is direct and the points of the scatter diagram are dispersed on either side of a straight line, the lines of regression are separate as shown in fig. 22. The case of greatest dispersion is when $\theta = 0$ and $r_{xy} = 0$. In this case the two regression lines coincide with the axes of X and Y.

If the correlation is inverse, θ is negative and the two lines of regression lie in the second and fourth quadrants instead of the first and third.

If the correlation is inverse and the points of the scatter diagram lie exactly on a straight line, the two regression lines coincide, $\theta = -45°$ and $r_{xy} = -1$.

We define $r_{xy} = s_{xy}/(s_x s_y)$ as the coefficient of correlation. Its values lie between $+1$ and -1 and are positive for direct correlation and negative for inverse correlation. A coefficient of $+1$ indicates perfect direct correlation, a coefficient of -1 perfect inverse correlation and a coefficient of 0 indicates complete absence of correlation.

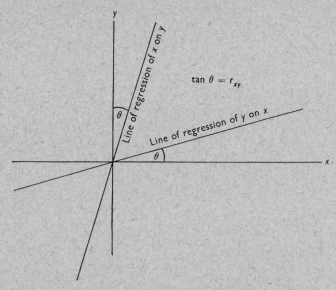

Fig. 22. The two regression lines when the units have been standardized and the mean of the array has been made the origin of co-ordinates.

132. The calculation of r_{xy}. The numerical value of r_{xy} can be calculated by the formula $r_{xy} = s_{xy}/(s_x s_y)$ where the covariance

$$s_{xy} = \frac{1}{n}\Sigma(x-\bar{x})(y-\bar{y}) \qquad \text{(see §127)}$$

$$= \text{the mean product of deviations,}$$

the standard deviation of the n values of x

$$s_x = \sqrt{\left\{\frac{\Sigma(x-\bar{x})^2}{n}\right\}}$$

and the standard deviation of the n values of y

$$s_y = \sqrt{\left\{\frac{\Sigma(y-\bar{y})^2}{n}\right\}}.$$

This procedure was used in *A First Course in Statistics*.

The more advanced student may prefer, however, to use

$$s_{xy} = \frac{\Sigma xy}{n} - \left(\frac{\Sigma x}{n}\right)\left(\frac{\Sigma y}{n}\right),$$

$$s_x = \sqrt{\left\{\frac{\Sigma x^2}{n} - \left(\frac{\Sigma x}{n}\right)^2\right\}},$$

$$s_y = \sqrt{\left\{\frac{\Sigma y^2}{n} - \left(\frac{\Sigma y}{n}\right)^2\right\}},$$

TABLE II A

The calculation of the coefficient of correlation r_{xy}
(working with an arbitrary origin and convenient units)

Millions of vehicles (working with 4·1 as origin and 0·1 as unit) x	Thousands of casualties (working with 201 as origin) y	x^2 (0·01 as unit)	y^2	xy (0·1 as unit)
-15	-63	225	3969	945
-10	-38	100	1444	380
-6	-35	36	1225	210
-4	-48	16	2304	192
0	-24	0	576	0
3	0	9	0	0
5	15	25	225	75
8	7	64	49	56
12	25	144	625	300
17	37	289	1369	629
$\Sigma x = 10$	$\Sigma y = -128$	$\Sigma x^2 = 908$	$\Sigma y^2 = 11786$	$\Sigma xy = 2787$

Covariance $\quad s_{xy} = \frac{\Sigma xy}{n} - \left(\frac{\Sigma x}{n}\right)\left(\frac{\Sigma y}{n}\right)$

$\qquad = 278\cdot7 - (1)(-12\cdot8)\quad$ with 0·1 as unit

$\qquad = 29\cdot15\quad$ in the original units.

Standard deviation of the 10 values of x

$$s_x = \sqrt{\left\{\frac{\Sigma x^2}{n} - \left(\frac{\Sigma x}{n}\right)^2\right\}}$$

$\qquad = \sqrt{\{90\cdot8 - (1)^2\}}\quad$ with 0·1 as unit

$\qquad = 0\cdot9476\quad$ in the original units.

Standard deviation of the 10 values of y

$$s_y = \sqrt{\left\{\frac{\Sigma y^2}{n} - \left(\frac{\Sigma y}{n}\right)^2\right\}}$$

$\qquad = \sqrt{\{1178\cdot6 - (-12\cdot8)^2\}}$

$\qquad = 31\cdot86\quad$ in the original units.

Coefficient of correlation

$\qquad r_{xy} = s_{xy}/(s_x . s_y)$

$\qquad = 0\cdot966,$

changing, if necessary, the origin and the units in order to minimize the amount of arithmetic. Table 11 A shows the calculation of r_{xy} by this second method for the bivariate distribution given in §120. Note that the xy values are not necessarily positive.

133. The coefficient of correlation and the regression lines for grouped data. At Raynes Park County Grammar School in 1950 a survey was made of the weights and heights of 248 boys between the ages of 11 and 16 years. Table 11 B is a classification of the results of the survey. The

TABLE IIB

Height of boy in in.	Weight of boy in stones									
	4–	5–	6–	7–	8–	9–	10–	11–	12–	13–
51–	—	1	—	—	—	—	—	—	—	—
54–	4	12	4	—	—	—	—	—	—	—
57–	—	22	21	3	—	—	—	—	—	—
60–	—	6	28	14	1	1	—	—	—	—
63–	—	1	1	24	17	4	—	—	1	—
66–	—	—	—	4	22	18	2	3	—	—
69–	—	—	—	—	1	14	10	4	—	—
72–	—	—	—	—	—	2	2	1	—	—
75–	—	—	—	—	—	—	—	—	—	—

number 28 in the table indicates, for example, that there were 28 boys of heights between 60 and 63 in. whose weights were between 6 and 7 stones (1 stone = 14 lb.). The calculation of r_{xy} from *grouped data* such as this is shown in table 11 C in which

(i) the central number in each *cell* is the frequency f of the (x, y) pair of values of the cell,

(ii) the upper left-hand italic number in each cell is the product xy of the (x, y) pair of values of the cell,

(iii) the lower right-hand italic number in each cell is the product-moment fxy of the cell found by multiplying the central number by the upper left-hand number.

By table 11 C, therefore,

the mean weight $\bar{x} = \Sigma f_x x / \Sigma f$

$\qquad = 48/248$ stones with $7\frac{1}{2}$ stones as origin

$\qquad = 7 \cdot 694$ stones;

the mean height $\bar{y} = \Sigma f_y y / \Sigma f$

$\qquad = 164/248$ 3-in. units with $61\frac{1}{2}$ in. as origin

$\qquad = 63 \cdot 48$ inches;

The calculation of the coefficient of correlation r_{xy} from grouped data

Note: each occupied cell shows three numbers — the deviation product xy (small, upper‑left), the frequency f (centre), and the product $f\cdot xy$ (lower‑right). Cells are written below as "xy / f / $f\,xy$".

Height of boy 61½ in. as origin and 3 in. as unit (y)	\(x=-3\)	\(-2\)	\(-1\)	\(0\)	\(1\)	\(2\)	\(3\)	\(4\)	\(5\)	Horizontal totals for each value of y f_y	First moment of each value of y $f_y y$	Second moment of each value of y $f_y y^2$
−3		6 / 1 / 6								1	− 3	9
−2	6 / 4 / 24	4 / 12 / 48	2 / 4 / 8							20	−40	80
−1		2 / 22 / 44	1 / 21 / 21	0 / 3 / 0						46	−46	46
0		0 / 6 / 0	0 / 28 / 0	0 / 14 / 0	0 / 1 / 0	0 / 1 / 0				50	0	0
1		−2 / 1 / −2	−1 / 1 / −1	0 / 24 / 0	1 / 17 / 17	2 / 4 / 8			5 / 1 / 5	48	48	48
2				0 / 4 / 0	2 / 22 / 44	4 / 18 / 72	6 / 2 / 12	8 / 3 / 24		49	98	196
3					3 / 1 / 3	6 / 14 / 84	9 / 10 / 90	12 / 4 / 48		29	87	261
4						8 / 2 / 16	12 / 2 / 24	16 / 1 / 16		5	20	80
Vertical total for each value of x f_x	4	42	54	45	41	39	14	8	1	$248 = \Sigma f$	$164 = \Sigma f_y y$	$720 = \Sigma f_y y^2$
First moment of each value of x $f_x x$	−12	−84	−54	0	41	78	42	32	5	$48 = \Sigma f_x x$		
Second moment of each value of x $f_x x^2$	36	168	54	0	41	156	126	128	25	$734 = \Sigma f_x x^2$		
Vertical total of product moments	24	96	28	0	64	180	126	88	5	$611 = \Sigma f xy$		

Weight of boy — 7½ stones as origin and 1 stone as unit (x).

the standard deviation of the x array

$$s_x = \sqrt{\left\{\frac{\Sigma f_x x^2}{\Sigma f} - \left(\frac{\Sigma f_x x}{\Sigma f}\right)^2\right\}}$$

$$= \sqrt{\left\{\frac{734}{248} - \left(\frac{48}{248}\right)^2\right\}} \quad \text{stones}$$

$$= 1 \cdot 710 \text{ stones};$$

the standard deviation of the y array

$$s_y = \sqrt{\left\{\frac{\Sigma f_y y^2}{\Sigma f} - \left(\frac{\Sigma f_y y}{\Sigma f}\right)^2\right\}}$$

$$= \sqrt{\left\{\frac{720}{248} - \left(\frac{164}{248}\right)^2\right\}} \quad \text{3-in. units}$$

$$= 4 \cdot 710 \text{ inches};$$

the covariance $\quad s_{xy} = \dfrac{\Sigma fxy}{\Sigma f} - \left(\dfrac{\Sigma f_x x}{\Sigma f}\right)\left(\dfrac{\Sigma f_y y}{\Sigma f}\right)$

$$= \frac{611}{248} - \left(\frac{48}{248}\right)\left(\frac{164}{248}\right) \quad \text{stone} \times \text{3-in. units}$$

$$= 7 \cdot 005 \text{ stone} \times \text{inch units.}$$

Hence the coefficient of correlation

$$r_{xy} = s_{xy}/(s_x \cdot s_y)$$

$$= 7 \cdot 005/(1 \cdot 710 \times 4 \cdot 710)$$

$$= 0 \cdot 87$$

and the least squares line of regression of x on y is

$$(x - \bar{x}) = \frac{s_{xy}}{s_y^2}(y - \bar{y}),$$

that is $\qquad x - 7 \cdot 694 = \dfrac{7 \cdot 005}{22 \cdot 18}(y - 63 \cdot 48)$

which may be written $\qquad x = 0 \cdot 32y - 12 \cdot 35.$

Note that the line of regression of x on y is of greater interest, in this case, than the line of regression of y on x. It enables us to state the average weight of a boy of given height.

134. The significance of r_{xy}. It was indicated in §131 that the coefficient of correlation r_{xy} lies between $+1$ and -1 and is positive for direct correlation and negative for inverse correlation. Values of r_{xy} near to unity indicate a high degree of correlation, values near to zero indicate an absence of correlation. When the value of r_{xy} has been calculated the question therefore arises 'Does $|r_{xy}|$ differ significantly from zero?' Table 11 D gives the $P = 5\%$ values of $|r_{xy}|$. If the calculated value of $|r_{xy}|$ is equal to or greater than the value given in the table for the appropriate number of (x,y) pairs, $|r_{xy}|$ differs significantly from zero. It differs from zero at the 5% level of significance. This means that the probability that no association exists between the variables is $\frac{1}{20}$.

TABLE II D
The $P = 5\%$ values of $|r_{xy}|$

No. of pairs of values of x and y from which r_{xy} is calculated	Minimum value of $|r_{xy}|$ for correlation to be probable	No. of pairs of values of x and y from which r_{xy} is calculated	Minimum value of $|r_{xy}|$ for correlation to be probable
6	0·82	14	0·54
7	0·76	15	0·52
8	0·71	16	0·50
9	0·67	18	0·47
10	0·64	20	0·45
11	0·61	40	0·31
12	0·58	80	0·22
13	0·56	100	0·20

135. Exercises.

1. Calculate r_{xy} for the bivariate distribution of §122.

2–5. Calculate the product-moment coefficients of correlation for the data given in exercises 1, 2, 3 and 6, §130.

6. The 1% sample of the 1951 Census shows the ages of husband and wife to be related as shown below:

Age of wife (y)	Age of husband (x)					
	20–	30–	40–	50–	60–	70–80
20–	12	7	—	—	—	—
30–	1	18	8	1	—	—
40–	—	2	19	6	1	—
50–	—	—	2	14	5	—
60–	—	—	—	1	8	2
70–80	—	—	—	—	1	3

(1 unit = 100,000 couples)

Calculate the coefficient of correlation r_{xy} and also the equation of the least squares line of regression of y on x.

Estimate the mean age of wife for husbands aged (i) 25, (ii) 45, (iii) 65.

7. *Associated TeleVision Limited. Charges in £ for 15-sec. advertisements*

Charge (£y) for a 15-sec. advertisement — Number (x) of homes viewing ATV programmes, in thousands

Charge (£y) for a 15-sec. advertisement	100–	200–	300–	400–	500–	600–	700–	800–
0–	6	—	—	—	—	—	—	—
50–	2	5	2	—	—	—	—	—
100–	5	7	3	1	1	—	—	—
150–	2	6	1	3	1	2	—	—
200–	1	17	7	0	1	0	—	—
250–	—	—	—	2	1	1	—	—
300–	—	—	—	—	1	1	—	—
350–	—	—	—	—	1	0	—	—
400–	—	—	—	—	—	3	1	—
450–	—	—	—	—	—	—	—	—

The above table shows how the charges for advertisements, £y, made by ATV were related to the number of homes viewing, x, during the autumn of 1956. Thus the number 17 in the table indicates that there were 17 cases in which the charge was between £200 and £250 when between 200,000 and 300,000 homes were viewing.

Calculate the coefficient of correlation r_{xy} and also the equation of the least squares line of regression of y on x.

Estimate the mean charge made by ATV for a 15-sec. advertisement at a time when half-a-million homes were viewing. [Northern]

12

Correlation by Ranks

136. The coefficient of rank correlation. Table 12A shows the data of §64 with *ranks* attached to the *x* and *y* values:

TABLE 12A

No. of vehicles (millions) *x*	Rank *X* of the *x* values	No. of casualties (thousands) *y*	Rank *Y* of the *y* values
2·6	10	138	10
3·1	9	163	8
3·5	8	166	7
3·7	7	153	9
4·1	6	177	6
4·4	5	201	5
4·6	4	216	3
4·9	3	208	4
5·3	2	226	2
5·8	1	238	1

The number 2·6, for example, is *tenth* in *order* or *rank* of the *x* values, 4·1 is *sixth* and 5·8 is *first*. If the product-moment coefficient of correlation is calculated from the ranks *X* and *Y* instead of the original values of *x* and *y* far less arithmetic is involved and an approximation to r_{xy} is obtained which is called the *coefficient of rank correlation, R*. This idea was originally introduced by C. Spearman in 1906. By applying the method shown in table 11A to the *X* and *Y* values the student will obtain *R* = 0·95.

137. The formula for the coefficient of rank correlation. The ranks are the numbers $1, 2, 3, 4, \ldots, n$ (*n* in the example under consideration being 10), and the algebraic formulae for the sum of the first *n* natural numbers and for the sum of their squares can be used to prove that *R* may be calculated as shown in table 12B by the formula

$$R = 1 - \frac{6\Sigma D^2}{n(n^2-1)},$$

where *D* is the *rank difference*.

TABLE 12B

Calculation of the coefficient of rank correlation (direct)

Rank of no. of vehicles X	Rank of no. of casualties Y	Rank difference X − Y D	D^2
10	10	0	0
9	8	1	1
8	7	1	1
7	9	−2	4
6	6	0	0
5	5	0	0
4	3	1	1
3	4	−1	1
2	2	0	0
1	1	0	0
	Total	0	8

Since $n = 10$ and $\Sigma D^2 = 8$,

$$R = 1 - 6 \times 8/10(10^2 - 1)$$

$$= 0\!\cdot\!95.$$

138. The derivation of the formula for the coefficient of rank correlation.

Suppose that $X_1, X_2, ..., X_n$ are the respective *ranks* of the n observations $x_1, x_2, ..., x_n$. Then $X_1, X_2, ..., X_n$ are the first n natural numbers $1, 2, ..., n$ (though not in order). Similarly if $Y_1, Y_2, ..., Y_n$ are the respective ranks of the n observations $y_1, y_2, ..., y_n$ then $Y_1, Y_2, ..., Y_n$ are the numbers $1, 2, ..., n$ (again not in order). It is proved in textbooks of algebra that

$$1 + 2 + 3 + ... + n = \tfrac{1}{2}n(n+1)$$

and

$$1^2 + 2^2 + 3^2 + ... + n^2 = \tfrac{1}{6}n(n+1)(2n+1).$$

Thus

$$\Sigma X = \tfrac{1}{2}n(n+1)$$

$$\Sigma X^2 = \tfrac{1}{6}n(n+1)(2n+1)$$

and

$$S_X^2 = \frac{\Sigma X^2}{n} - \left(\frac{\Sigma X}{n}\right)^2$$

$$= \frac{(n+1)(2n+1)}{6} - \frac{(n+1)^2}{4}.$$

Moreover, as $Y_1, Y_2, ..., Y_n$ represent the same numbers as $X_1, X_2, ..., X_n$ though not in the same order

$$S_X^2 = S_Y^2.$$

Now the rank differences $D_1, D_2, ..., D_n$ are given by

$$D_1 = (X_1 - Y_1), \quad D_2 = (X_2 - Y_2), \quad ..., \quad D_n = (X_n - Y_n)$$

and $\quad \Sigma D^2 = (X_1 - Y_1)^2 + (X_2 - Y_2)^2 + \dots + (X_n - Y_n)^2$

$$= (X_1^2 + X_2^2 + \dots + X_n^2) - 2(X_1 Y_1 + X_2 Y_2 + \dots + X_n Y_n)$$

$$+ (Y_1^2 + Y_2^2 + \dots + Y_n^2)$$

$$= \tfrac{1}{6} n(n+1)(2n+1) - 2\Sigma XY + \tfrac{1}{6} n(n+1)(2n+1).$$

Thus $\quad \Sigma XY = \tfrac{1}{6} n(n+1)(2n+1) - \tfrac{1}{2}\Sigma D^2$

and $\quad S_{XY} = \dfrac{\Sigma XY}{n} - \left(\dfrac{\Sigma X}{n}\right)\left(\dfrac{\Sigma Y}{n}\right)$

$$= \tfrac{1}{6}(n+1)(2n+1) - \dfrac{1}{2n}\Sigma D^2 - \tfrac{1}{4}(n+1)^2.$$

Hence the coefficient of rank correlation

$$R = \dfrac{S_{XY}}{S_X S_Y}$$

$$= \dfrac{\tfrac{1}{6}(n+1)(2n+1) - \tfrac{1}{4}(n+1)^2 - \dfrac{1}{2n}\Sigma D^2}{\tfrac{1}{6}(n+1)(2n+1) - \tfrac{1}{4}(n+1)^2}$$

$$= 1 - \dfrac{\dfrac{1}{2n}\Sigma D^2}{\tfrac{1}{6}(n+1)(2n+1) - \tfrac{1}{4}(n+1)^2}$$

$$= 1 - \dfrac{6\Sigma D^2}{n(n^2 - 1)}.$$

Note that, where n is large, this formula approximates to

$$R = 1 - \dfrac{6\Sigma D^2}{n^3}$$

because n is negligible compared with n^3.

139. Method of ranking equal values of a variate. If the *cinema admissions (millions)* of §122 are arranged in descending order of magnitude they appear as follows:

11·0, 10·5, 10·0, 10·0, 9·9, 9·7, 9·4, 9·4, 9·3, 9·3, 9·0, 8·6.

The rank of 11·0 is, therefore, 1 and that of 10·5 is 2. The rank of the *two* values 10·0 is not taken as 3 or 4 but as 3·5, the mean of the ranks 3 and 4. Similarly, the ranks of the two values 9·4 is taken as 7·5 and that of the two values 9·3 as 9·5. The twelve ranks are thus:

1, 2, 3·5, 3·5, 5, 6, 7·5, 7·5, 9·5, 9·5, 11, 12

and their sum is 78, the same as the sum of the ranks

1, 2, 3, 4, 5, 6, 7, 8, 9, 10, 11, 12

when the values of the variate are all different.

8

Table 12c shows the method of calculating the coefficient or rank correlation for the *cinema admissions*, x, and *TV licences, y*, of §122. It is a good example of inverse correlation. The value obtained, $R = -0.84$, is considerably higher (numerically) than the value $r_{xy} = -0.75$ obtained from the original (x, y) values of §122. It must be clearly understood that table 11D is for minimum values of $|r_{xy}|$. No similar table exists for minimum values of $|R|$. Indeed, R is nothing more than a quickly calculated approximation to r_{xy}. It must be realised, however, that the coefficient of rank correlation has one distinct advantage in that it can be used when the two variables to be compared cannot be measured. Exercise 1, §140 is an example in which depths of colour are ranked in order although it is quite impossible to measure them by any form of graduated scale.

TABLE 12C
Calculation of the coefficient of rank correlation (inverse)

Cinema admissions		TV licences		Rank difference	
(Millions)	Rank	Per 1000 population	Rank	$X - Y$	
x	X	y	Y	D	D^2
11·0	1	12	12	−11	121
10·0	$3\frac{1}{2}$	18	11	$-7\frac{1}{2}$	$56\frac{1}{4}$
10·0	$3\frac{1}{2}$	24	10	$-6\frac{1}{2}$	$42\frac{1}{4}$
9·4	$7\frac{1}{2}$	37	9	$-1\frac{1}{2}$	$2\frac{1}{4}$
10·5	2	52	8	− 6	36
9·7	6	64	7	− 1	1
9·4	$7\frac{1}{2}$	69	6	$1\frac{1}{2}$	$2\frac{3}{4}$
9·3	$9\frac{1}{2}$	81	5	$4\frac{1}{2}$	$20\frac{1}{4}$
9·9	5	98	4	1	1
9·3	$9\frac{1}{2}$	101	3	$6\frac{1}{2}$	$42\frac{1}{4}$
9·0	11	106	2	9	81
8·6	12	119	1	11	121
			Total	0	$526\frac{1}{2}$

Since $n = 12$ and $\Sigma D^2 = 526\frac{1}{2}$

$$R = 1 - 6 \times 526\frac{1}{2} / 12(12^2 - 1)$$

$$= -0.84.$$

140. Exercises.

1. Ten shades of the colour green when arranged in their true order from light to dark are numbered 1–10 respectively. An observer, when asked to arrange the shades from light to dark, produces the following rank

$$3, \quad 1, \quad 5, \quad 2, \quad 6, \quad 4, \quad 10, \quad 9, \quad 7, \quad 8.$$

What is the value of Spearman's coefficient of rank correlation in this case?
[London]

2. In a drama competition 10 plays were ranked by two adjudicators as follows:

Play	A	B	C	D	E	F	G	H	J	K
Rank given by X	5	2	6	8	1	7	4	9	3	10
Rank given by Y	1	7	6	10	4	5	3	8	2	9

Calculate the coefficient of ranked correlation. Is there any reason for saying that there is a significant agreement between the two adjudicators?

[London]

3–6. Calculate the coefficients of rank correlation for the data given in exercises 1, 2, 3 and 6, §130.

13

Miscellaneous Exercises

1. Part of a turbo-alternator test routine carried out at an Electric Power Station included observations of manometer readings at timed intervals. Two sets of readings were taken by two observers A and B using separate manometers. Both instruments were connected to the same orifice plate in the condensate line and observations were made alternately, at 15-sec. intervals, by A and B. The following table summarises the two sets of readings made by the observers:

Manometer reading (inches of mercury)	Frequency	
	Observer A	Observer B
12·0–12·4	1	1
12·4–12·8	5	3
12·8–13·2	16	14
13·2–13·6	13	15
13·6–14·0	25	18
14·0–14·4	26	11
14·4–14·8	11	18
14·8–15·2	9	24
15·2–15·6	8	13
15·6–16·0	3	2
16·0–16·4	3	1
Total	120	120

Calculate the mean and the standard deviation of each set of readings.

2. Using the means and standard deviations obtained in Ex. 1 above, make out a table of expected frequencies (for the same class intervals as Ex. 1 above) based on the null hypothesis that each distribution is normal.

3. Using the observed and expected frequencies of Ex. 1 and 2 above, calculate values of χ^2 for each set of observations and hence show that the readings made by observer A did not differ significantly from normal, but those made by observer B did. Assuming that both observers were reliable what might be inferred about the manometers?

4. Obtain the 95 % confidence limits of the mean of the readings made by observer A in Ex. 1 above.

5. Estimate the level of significance of the difference between the means of the two sets of readings in Ex. 1 above. (NOTE: This assumes that each set of 120 readings is normally distributed.)

6. A bridge player knows that his two opponents hold a total of 6 trump cards. If the cards are distributed at random, calculate the probability that neither of the opponents holds (i) more than 3 trump cards, (ii) more than 4 trump cards. [Cambridge]

7. In an examination the probability that candidate A will solve a given problem is $\frac{1}{4}$ and the probability that candidate B will solve it is $\frac{2}{3}$. What is the probability that the examiner will receive a correct solution from either A or B or from both assuming that they work independently? [Cambridge]

8. A bag contains 20 black balls and 15 white balls. (i) If 2 balls are withdrawn in succession, what is the probability that one is black and the other is white? (ii) If a sample of 5 balls is taken what is the probability that at least 4 are black? [Cambridge]

9. Two surveyors make repeated observations of the same angle. Their readings differ only in the figure for seconds of angle with the following results:

Surveyor	No. of observations	Mean reading (sec.)	Standard deviation (sec.)
A	6	38	4·33
B	8	34	3·21

Do these data provide evidence that there is a significant difference between the observations of A and B (i) at the 10 % level, and (ii) at the 5 % level of significance? [Cambridge]

10. The mean number of interruptions per hour to which a person is subjected during his normal working day is 4. Estimate the probabilities that in any particular hour he is interrupted (i) 4 times, (ii) not more than 4 times. [Cambridge]

11. Using the method of least squares, obtain the equation of the best straight line through the 3 following points:

x	0	1	2
y	2·3	6·5	10·6

[Cambridge]

12. An automatic machine produces bolts whose diameters are required to lie within the range 0·496 in. to 0·504 in. A sample of 10 bolts is found to have a mean diameter of 0·498 in. and a standard deviation of 0·002 in. If the diameters are normally distributed, is there evidence, at the 5 % level, of an error in setting the machine?
If the machine is adjusted to produce bolts with a mean diameter of 0·500 in., what proportion of bolts is likely to be rejected on full inspection? It may be assumed that the standard deviation of the diameters is not affected by the adjustment. [Cambridge]

13. It is found that on the average a certain electronic computer makes a mistake every 10 min. If the mistakes occur at random intervals, calculate the probability of no mistakes occurring in a calculation lasting (i) 5 min., (ii) 30 min. [Cambridge]

14. The relationship between the output voltage V in millivolts and the temperature difference θ in ° C. of a thermocouple is given approximately by the formula

$$V = a\left(\frac{\theta}{100}\right) + b\left(\frac{\theta}{100}\right)^2.$$

Use the method of least squares to derive equations which determine the best values of a and b from the following experimental results:

θ (° C.)	100	200	300	400
V (millivolts)	0·95	1·40	1·12	0·20

[Cambridge]

15. The following contingency table was drawn up from the records of a firm which manufactures transformers:

	No. of transformers found satisfactory at first examination	No. of transformers found unsatisfactory at first examination
Department A	15	5
Department B	10	10

Do these figures provide conclusive evidence that the work done by department A is better than that done by department B?

16. Prove that, if f is the frequency of a measurement x, the mean of the measurements is M and x_0 is any number, then the standard deviation σ is given by

$$\sigma^2 = \frac{1}{N}\Sigma f(x - x_0)^2 - (x_0 - M)^2,$$

where $N = \Sigma f$. [London]

17. Show that the probability of exactly r successes in n trials is the coefficient of t^r in the expansion of $(1 - p + pt)^n$, where p is the probability of success in any one trial.

On an expedition, a machine is taken which fails to start on the average once in c attempts owing to the breakage of a certain part. If s spare parts of this kind are carried, show that the probability that the last spare part will fail at the nth attempt at starting is equal to the coefficient of t^s in the expansion of

$$\frac{1}{c}\left(1 + \frac{t-1}{c}\right)^{n-1}.$$

[London]

18. If the points with co-ordinates $(x_1, y_1), (x_2, y_2), \ldots, (x_n, y_n)$ lie approximately on the straight line $y = ax + b$, show how to determine the values of the constants a and b which will make the sum

$$\sum_{r=1}^{n} (y_r - ax_r - b)^2$$

a minimum.

Find the equation of the straight line which satisfies this condition for the set of points with co-ordinates

$$(0, 13), \quad (3, 10), \quad (6, 8), \quad (9, 5), \quad (12, 2).$$

[London]

19. In an experiment which can succeed or fail, the probability of success is p and of failure is q, where $p+q = 1$. Show that the probability of r successful experiments in n attempts is given by the term in p^r in the binomial expansion of $(q+p)^n$.

In the manufacture of screws by a certain process it was found that 5 % of the screws were rejected because they failed to satisfy tolerance requirements. What was the probability that a sample of 12 screws contained (i) exactly 2, (ii) not more than 2 rejects? [London]

20. Use the method of least squares to find the values of a and b which nearly satisfy the four equations

$$2a+b = 2{\cdot}76, \qquad 4a+3b = 3{\cdot}90,$$
$$3a-b = 8{\cdot}62, \qquad a+2b = -1{\cdot}38. \qquad \text{[London]}$$

21. A competition consists of filling in a form which contains N spaces and each space has to be filled up in one of n ways. There is a unique correct solution. If the spaces are filled up in a random manner, prove that the probability of there being r mistakes is the coefficient of x^r in the expansion of

$$n^{-N}\{1+x(n-1)\}^N.$$

If $N = 12$ and $n = 3$ prove that the probability of there being *not more* than 2 mistakes is $289{\cdot}3^{-12}$. [London]

22. If σ is the standard deviation and μ the mean of the data in a given statistical table, and if σ_1^2 is the mean of the squares of the deviations from an assumed mean a, show that

$$\sigma^2 = \sigma_1^2-(\mu-a)^2.$$

The annual salaries of a group of employees are given in the following table, in which £S is the salary and N is the number receiving each amount:

S	450	500	550	600	650	700	750	800
N	3	5	8	7	9	7	4	7

Calculate the mean salary and standard deviation. [London]

23. If the points with co-ordinates $(x_i, y_i), (i = 1, 2, ..., n)$ lie approximately on a straight line $y = mx+c$, find the values of m and c in terms of Σx, Σy, Σx^2 and Σxy if the sum $\sum_{i=1}^{n} (y_i - mx_i - c)^2$ is a minimum.

Hence find the values of m and c for the case where (x_i, y_i) are given by $(1,14)$, $(2,11)$, $(3,8)$, $(5,4)$, $(6,0)$ and deduce the best value of y corresponding to $x = 4$. [London]

24. The yield of a chemical process was measured at 3 temperatures, each with 2 concentrations of a particular reactant, as recorded below:

Temperature ($t°$ C.)	40	40	50	50	60	60
Concentration (x)	0·2	0·4	0·2	0·4	0·2	0·4
Yield (y)	38	42	41	46	46	49

Use the method of least squares to find the best values of the coefficients a, b, c in the equation $\qquad y = a+bt+cx,$

119

and from your equation estimate the yield at $70°$ C. with concentration 0.5.
[London]

HINT: To obtain the three normal equations for a, b and c differentiate $\Sigma(y-a-bt-cx)^2$ (i) with respect to a, (ii) with respect to b, (iii) with respect to c and equate each differential coefficient to zero.

25. The mean of 50 readings of a variable was 7.43, and their standard deviation was 0.28. The following 10 additional readings become available: 6.80, 7.81, 7.58, 7.70, 8.05, 6.98, 7.78, 7.85, 7.21, 7.40.

If these are included with the original 50 readings find (i) the mean, (ii) the standard deviation of the whole set of 60 readings. [London]

26. Calculate the mean and variance of the binomial distribution in which the distribution of the relative frequencies (the total frequency is unity) of $0, 1, 2, \ldots, n$ successes in n events consists of the terms in the expansion of $(q+p)^n$, where $q+p = 1$, q being the chance of failure and p of success in each event.

Two ounces of seeds of yellow wallflowers are thoroughly mixed before sowing with 8 oz. of seeds of red wallflowers and eventually the plants are bedded out in rows of 20. Estimate the mean and variance of the number of yellow flowers in each row. [Northern]

27. Calculate the mean value of $10 \cos \theta$ over the range $0 \leqslant \theta \leqslant \pi/2$, giving the result in terms of π.

The distance between adjacent printed lines on a sheet of writing paper is $\frac{1}{2}$ in. The paper is laid flat on a horizontal table and a straight needle 5 in. long is thrown at random 40 times on to the paper. The following table shows the frequency distribution of the number of intersections of the printed lines made by the needle as it lies on the table after each throw:

No. of intersections	0	1	2	3	4	5	6	7	8	9	10
Frequency	3	4	1	3	1	1	4	4	6	6	7

Calculate the mean number of intersections.

Combine the mean value obtained in the first part of this question with the mean obtained in the second to estimate the value of π, explaining by means of a diagram the principle involved. [Northern]

28. A variable x is distributed at random between the values 0 and 1 so that the equation of the frequency curve is

$$y = Ax^2(1-x)^3,$$

where A is a constant. Find the value of A such that the area under the frequency curve $\int_0^1 y\,dx$ is unity.

Using this value of A determine

(i) the mean, $\bar{x} = \int_0^1 xy\,dx$,

(ii) the variance, $\sigma^2 = \int_0^1 x^2 y\,dx - \bar{x}^2$.

NOTE: For a *continuous distribution* such as this $\int y\,dx$, $\int xy\,dx$ and $\int x^2 y\,dx$ correspond to Σf, Σfx and Σfx^2 in a discrete frequency distribution.

29. A variable x is distributed at random between the values 0 and 4 so that the equation of the frequency curve is

$$y = Ax^3(4-x)^2,$$

where A is a constant. Find the value of A such that the area under the frequency curve is unity. Determine the mean and standard deviation of the distribution. [Northern]

30. A variate x can assume values only between 0 and 1, and the equation of its frequency curve is

$$y = Ae^{-2x} \quad (0 < x < 1),$$

where A is a constant such that the area under the curve is unity. Determine the value of A to three decimal places. Calculate the mean and variance of the distribution. [Northern]

31. A variate x can assume values only between 0 and a, and the equation of its frequency curve is

$$y = A(a-x)^2 \quad (0 \leqslant x \leqslant a),$$

where A and a are constants such that the area under the curve and the mean of the distribution are both unity. Determine the numerical values of A and a and find the 10th and 90th percentiles of the distribution. [Northern]

32. If n is a positive integer show that $\int_0^\infty x^n e^{-x} dx = n!$

A variate has for its frequency distribution curve the graph of $y = xe^{-x/a}$ for $x > 0$, where $a > 0$. Find the total frequency, the mean and the standard deviation of the variate. [London]

33. The length x of the side of a square is rectangularly distributed between 1 and 2. Show that the area y of the square is distributed between 1 and 4 with a probability distribution $p(y)dy = \frac{1}{2}y^{-\frac{1}{2}}dy$.

Sketch the frequency curve, and calculate the mean and variance of the area of the square.

HINT: For the rectangular distribution, $p(x)dx = A dx$ (A constant).

But $\int_1^2 p(x)dx = 1$ and thus $A = 1$. Now $x = y^{\frac{1}{2}}$ and hence

$$\int_1^2 dx = \int_1^4 \frac{1}{2}y^{-\frac{1}{2}}dy.$$

34. The length x of the edge of a cube is rectangularly distributed between 5 and 10. Show that the volume y of the cube is distributed between 125 and 1000 with a probability distribution $p(y)dy = \frac{1}{15}y^{-\frac{2}{3}}dy$.

Sketch the frequency curve, and calculate the mean and variance of the volume of the cube. [Northern]

35. The radius x of a circle is rectangularly distributed between 1 and 2. Show that the area y of the circle is distributed between π and 4π with probability distribution $p(y)dy = \frac{1}{2}\pi^{-\frac{1}{2}}y^{-\frac{1}{2}}dy.$

Sketch the probability curve and calculate the mean and the variance of the area of the circle. [Northern]

36. (i) A variate x can take the values $1, 2, 3, \ldots, n$ with equal probability. Calculate the standard deviation of x.

(ii) The standard deviations of two samples, each of n observations, are s_1 and s_2, their respective means being m_1 and m_2. Show that the standard deviation s of the combined sample of $2n$ observations is given by

$$s^2 = \tfrac{1}{2}(s_1^2 + s_2^2) + \tfrac{1}{4}(m_1 - m_2)^2. \qquad \text{[Northern]}$$

37. (i) A variate x can take the values $1, 2, 3, \ldots, n$, with probabilities proportional to $1, 2, 3, \ldots, n$ respectively. Calculate the mean value of x.

(ii) Two samples, consisting of n_1 and n_2 observations, have means m_1 and m_2 and standard deviations s_1 and s_2 respectively. Show that the standard deviation s of the combined sample of $(n_1 + n_2)$ observations is given by

$$s^2 = \frac{n_1 s_1^2 + n_2 s_2^2}{n_1 + n_2} + \frac{n_1 n_2 (m_1 - m_2)^2}{(n_1 + n_2)^2}. \qquad \text{[Northern]}$$

38. When A and B play chess, the chance of either winning a game is $\tfrac{1}{4}$ and the chance of the game being drawn is $\tfrac{1}{2}$. Find the chance of A winning at least three games out of five.

Also, if A and B play a match to be decided as soon as either has won two games, find the chance of the match being finished in ten games or less.

[Northern]

39. If $\phi(x) = \dfrac{1}{\sqrt{(2\pi)}}\, e^{-\frac{1}{2}x^2}$, show that $x^n \phi(x) \to 0$ when $x \to \infty$.

Evaluate $\displaystyle\int_{-\infty}^{\infty} |x|\, \phi(x)\, dx.$

Also, assuming that $\displaystyle\int_{-\infty}^{\infty} \phi(x)\, dx = 1$, evaluate $\displaystyle\int_{-\infty}^{\infty} x^2 \phi(x)\, dx$. Hence obtain, for the distribution $\phi(x)$, the ratio of the mean deviation to the standard deviation.

[Northern]

40. The two equal sides of an isosceles triangle are each of unit length and the angle θ between them is rectangularly distributed between 0 and $\pi/6$. Show that the area y of the triangle is distributed between 0 and $\tfrac{1}{4}$ with probability distribution

$$p(y)\, dy = \frac{12}{\pi}(1 - 4y^2)^{-\frac{1}{2}}\, dy.$$

Sketch the probability curve and calculate the mean and variance of the area of the triangle. [Northern]

41. The journey by air from one city centre A to another city centre B is divided into five stages and the means and standard deviations of the time taken for each stage are shown in the following table:

The five stages of the journey	Mean time (min.)	Standard deviation (min.)
Motor-coach journey from city centre A to air terminal A	35	2
Wait at air terminal A	12	2
Air journey from air terminal A to air terminal B	65	4
Wait at air terminal B	8	1
Motor-coach journey from air terminal B to city centre B	25	2

Assuming that the times taken for each stage of the journey are independently normally distributed, calculate the mean and standard deviation of the time taken for the whole journey.

Estimate the probability of the whole journey taking (i) less than $2\frac{1}{4}$ hr., (ii) more than $2\frac{3}{4}$ hr. [Northern]

42. In a certain school the age of each of 500 boys and his percentage mark in a general knowledge test were recorded. The relationship between the number pairs thus obtained is shown in the following table:

Percentage mark (y)	Age in years (x)									
	10	11	12	13	14	15	16	17	18	19
80–89	—	—	—	—	—	—	—	2	—	—
70–79	—	—	—	—	3	2	6	3	4	1
60–69	—	—	—	10	15	26	19	14	2	—
50–59	—	2	7	32	43	23	7	2	0	1
40–49	—	2	28	50	31	15	2	1	—	—
30–39	—	10	32	38	6	1	—	—	—	—
20–29	—	11	28	4	—	—	—	—	—	—
10–19	3	7	7	—	—	—	—	—	—	—

(i) Calculate the coefficient of correlation r_{xy} for the age in years x and the percentage mark y.

(ii) Obtain, by the method of least squares, the equation

$$y = mx + c$$

of the line of regression of y on x. [Northern]

43. A hundred samples, each of 12 articles, are drawn at random from a large bulk of articles, all of which should be alike, but 10 % of which are in fact defective. Estimate the number of samples in which you would expect the number of defective articles to be (i) 0, (ii) 1, (iii) 2, (iv) 3 or more.
[Northern]

44. A man who was trying out various makes of razor blade kept a record of the number of shaves x he got from each blade before he had to discard it. For 50 blades of one make he found that x was approximately normally distributed with mean 7·2 and standard deviation 2·0. Draw the frequency curve for this distribution, taking a scale of 1 in. to two shaves per blade and making the area under the curve 5 sq. in.

For 50 blades of a different make he obtained the following distribution:

x	5	6	7	8	9	10	11	12	13	14
Frequency	1	2	4	6	9	9	8	6	3	2

On the same diagram as before draw a histogram of area 5 sq. in. to represent the new distribution. Describe in words any inference that can be made from the two distributions. [Northern]

45. Calculate the number of different selections of three letters that can be made from the 10 letters of the word MANCHESTER.

Find, in addition, the probability that any one selection of three letters will contain (i) just one E, (ii) at least one E.

46. The following table is taken from a recent report on the serving of school dinners in grammar schools of Great Britain:

Time taken for school dinner in minutes	20	25	30	35	40	Total
No. of girls' schools	5	19	125	65	49	263
No. of co-educational schools	10	35	121	56	44	266

Calculate the mean and standard deviation of the times taken (i) in girls' schools, (ii) in co-educational schools.

Determine whether or not the difference between the means is significant.

47. In determining the nature and seriousness of an illness a common hospital procedure is to measure the *Erythrocyte Sedimentation Rate* (*E.S.R.*), using a solution of sodium citrate and fresh venous blood from the patient. The citrate prevents the blood from clotting and is called the *anticoagulant*. For other haematological tests sequestrin is often used as the anticoagulant. The question arises: Is it satisfactory to determine the *E.S.R.* by citrating blood which has already been collected in sequestrin? In order to try to answer this question the *E.S.R.*'s of 20 patients, all seriously ill, were determined (i) by using sodium citrate alone, and (ii) by using sodium citrate mixed with sequestrin. The following table gives the results:

Patient	1	2	3	4	5	6	7	8	9	10
E.S.R. (i) (sod. cit. alone) x	79	38	26	77	37	125	68	22	117	32
E.S.R. (ii) (sod. cit.+sequestrin) y	83	44	45	82	41	125	69	24	121	31

Patient	11	12	13	14	15	16	17	18	19	20
E.S.R. (i) (sod. cit. alone) x	82	20	32	41	99	81	105	145	145	6
E.S.R. (ii) (sod. cit.+sequestrin) y	80	20	38	47	78	83	114	143	143	6

Calculate the mean and the standard deviation of the differences between x and y and determine whether or not the mean of the differences differs significantly from zero.

Suppose it is decided that the readings of patients no. 3 and no. 15 are erroneous and that they should be ignored, determine whether or not the mean of the differences of the other 18 pairs of readings differs significantly from zero. [Northern]

48. Given that the mean and the standard deviation of the n values

$$x_1, x_2, x_3, \ldots, x_n$$

are $\bar{x}$ and s respectively, obtain the mean and the standard deviation of the n values $(ax_1+b), (ax_2+b), (ax_3+b), \ldots, (ax_n+b)$.

The marks gained by a group of candidates in a certain subject in an examination had a mean of 42 and a standard deviation of 7. Obtain a formula for converting the marks so as to make the mean 50 and the standard deviation 10.

If a scholarship is to be awarded on the marks obtained in three subjects, explain why conversions such as the above applied to the three separate sheets of marks would help in making the award. [Northern]

49. A variate x can assume values only between 0 and 5 and the equation of its frequency curve is
$$y = A \sin \tfrac{1}{5}\pi x \quad (0 \leqslant x \leqslant 5),$$
where A is a constant such that the area under the curve is unity. Determine the value of A and obtain the median and quartiles of the distribution.

Show also that the variance of the distribution is
$$50 \left\{ \frac{1}{8} - \frac{1}{\pi^2} \right\}. \qquad \text{[Northern]}$$

50. A box contains 36 batteries of which 4 are defective. If a random sample of 5 batteries is drawn from the box, calculate, correct to three places of decimals, the probability of the number of defective batteries in the sample being (i) 0, (ii) 1, (iii) more than 1. [Northern]

Answers to Exercises

Preliminary Revision Exercises

1. 63·9; 1·6. **2.** 21·6; 1·8. **3.** 10; $\sqrt{2}.\frac{1}{2}\sqrt{3}$. **4.** 10·2.

5. 49·5; 7·4. **6.** $\dfrac{n_1 M_1 + n_2 M_2}{n_1 + n_2}$; $\left\{\dfrac{n_1\sigma_1^2 + n_2\sigma_2^2}{n_1 + n_2}\right\}^{\frac{1}{2}}$.

7. 3·83; 78·7; 29·4. **8.** 2·1 (late); 3·3; $5\frac{1}{2}$, $-1(5\cdot4, -1\cdot2)$.

9. 50, 20, 21, 43, 61, 74. **10.** $y = (\frac{5}{4})x - 35$.

$\bar{y} = (\frac{5}{4})\bar{x} - 35$; $s' = (\frac{5}{4})s$.

11. 10·55; 2·475 **12.** $5\frac{5}{6}$; 6·8.
To fall (to 10·5).

§11. **1.** (i) 0·01; (ii) 0·61; (iii) 9·94; (iv) 39·44; (v) 39·44; (vi) 9·94; (vii) 0·61; (viii) 0·01.

2. 0·03, 0·79, 7·26, 26·38, 38·11, 21·95, 5·01, 0·47.

3. 0·13, 8·99, 53·94, 34·67, 2·22, 0·01.

4. 9, 63, 156, 131, 37, 4.

§14. **1.** (i) 1·97; (ii) 5·29. **2.** (i) 9·12; (ii) 2·28.

3. 3·00 in. 0·01216 in. (i) 10·9 over $+10·9$ under;

(ii) 1·99 over $+1·99$ under.

4. 108 ohms, 92 ohms. **6.** £53.

§25. **1.** $\frac{11}{24}$. **2.** (i) $\frac{23}{100}$; (ii) $\frac{379}{1800}$. **3.** 0·46. **4.** $\frac{1}{120}$.

5. (i) $\frac{1}{1296}$; (ii) $\frac{19}{1296}$; (iii) $\frac{523}{648}$.

6. $\frac{216}{671}$, $\frac{180}{671}$, $\frac{150}{671}$, $\frac{125}{671}$. Total = 1.

§33. **1.** (i) 3136; (ii) 2296; $\frac{3}{8}$. **2.** $\frac{9}{14}$.

3. (i) $2^9.3^{16}.17.19/5^{20} = 0\cdot07$;

(ii) $3^{10}(2^{12}.11.13.17.19. + 2^9.3^6.17.19 + 3^{10})/5^{20} = 0\cdot19$.

4. $\frac{8}{35}$; $\frac{1}{2}$;

1	$\frac{1}{2}$	0	$-\frac{1}{2}$	-1
$\frac{1}{70}$	$\frac{16}{70}$	$\frac{36}{70}$	$\frac{16}{70}$	$\frac{1}{70}$

5. $\frac{1}{4}$; $\frac{21}{100}$ **6.** (i) $\frac{1}{285}$; (ii) $\frac{1}{57}$; (iii) $\frac{32}{57}$.

§36. **1.** $\frac{125}{216}, \frac{75}{216}, \frac{15}{216}, \frac{1}{216}$; 125, 75, 15, 1.

2. $\frac{3125}{7776}, \frac{3125}{7776}, \frac{1250}{7776}, \frac{250}{7776}, \frac{25}{7776}, \frac{1}{7776}$. 40·2, 40·2, 16·1, 3·2, 0·3, 0·0.

§38. $\frac{1}{16}, \frac{4}{16}, \frac{6}{16}, \frac{4}{16}, \frac{1}{16}$; 2·5, 10, 15, 10, 2·5.

§40. **1.** 59·0, 32·8, 7·3, 0·9. **2.** 60·3, 30·9, 7·5, 1·3.

§43. **1.** (i) 0·15; (ii) 0·96. **2.** 4, 11, 14, 11, 6, 3, 1.

3. (i) 0·0083; (ii) 0·2803. **4.** $\frac{864}{3125}$; $\frac{513}{625}$.

5. (i) $\frac{1}{3375}$; (ii) 0·339. **6.** $\frac{280}{2187} = 0·128$.

§48. **1.** 0·24, 0·048. **2.** $18\frac{3}{4}\%$.

§50. (i) 0·132, 0·266, 0·268, 0·178, 0·089, 0·067. (ii) 0·135, 0·271, 0·271, 0·180, 0·090, 0·053.

§55. **1.** 60·7%, 9·0%. **2.** 0·9048, 0·0905, 0·0047.

3. 0·3679, 0·3679, 0·1840, 0·0613, 0·0189.

4. 0·6065, 0·3033, 0·0902. **5.** (i) 0·0498; (ii) 0·3526.

6. 0·0069. **7.** 0·6703. **8.** $m = 1·87, s = 1·76$.

9. $m = 0·128, s = 0·366$; 20941, 2680, 172, 7, 0, 0.

10. $m = 1·182, s = 1·167$, 397 or 398.

11. 22·3%, 19·1%, 16·7%, 18·6%.

§63. **1.** $m = 48·8, s = 12·5$; E's are 14, 53, 123, 155, 106, 40, 9. $\nu = 4$, $\chi^2 = 20·4$, distribution not normal.

2. $m = 35·7, s = 1·96$; E's are 11, 73, 276, 387, 207, 46. $\nu = 3, \chi^2 = 2·9$, distribution normal.

3. $m = 67·5, s = 2·54$; E's are 38, 124, 261, 300, 193, 69, 15. $\nu = 4$, $\chi^2 = 1·4$, distribution normal.

4. $m = 8·12, s = 0·0855$; E's are 5, 78, 333, 415, 152, 17. $\nu = 3$, $\chi^2 = 14·2$, distribution not normal.

§65. **1.** $p = 0·1875, n = 6$; E's are 11·5, 16, 12·5; $\nu = 1, \chi^2 = 0·04$, distribution binomial.

2. $p = \frac{1}{12}, n = 12$; E's are 17, 19, 14; $\nu = 1, \chi^2 = 0·13$, distribution binomial.

3. E's are 14, 22, 16, 8; $\nu = 3, \chi^2 = 0·54$, distribution binomial.

4. E's are 11, 32, 40, 26, 11; $\nu = 4, \chi^2 = 5·35$, distribution binomial.

5. E's are 26, 130, 260, 130, 26; $\nu = 5, \chi^2 = 3·36$, distribution binomial.

§68. 1. E's are 14, 24, 22, 14, 18; $\nu = 3$, $\chi^2 = 4 \cdot 8$, distribution Poisson.

2. E's are 20941, 2680, 172, 7, 0, 0; $\nu = 2$, $\chi^2 = 23$, not Poisson.

3. E's are 336, 398, 235, 93, 27, 7; $\nu = 4$, $\chi^2 = 18$, not Poisson.

4. E's are 13, 15, 12; $\nu = 1$, $\chi^2 = 0 \cdot 14$, distribution Poisson.

5. E's are 18, 18, 14; $\nu = 1$, $\chi^2 = 0 \cdot 13$, distribution Poisson.

6. E's are 16, 21, 14, 9; $\nu = 2$, $\chi^2 = 0 \cdot 16$, distribution Poisson.

7. E's are 16, 32, 32, 22, 18; $\nu = 3$, $\chi^2 = 7 \cdot 6$, distribution Poisson.

8. E's are 68, 171, 213, 179, 111, 90; $\nu = 4$, $\chi^2 \doteqdot 140$, not Poisson.

§76. 1. (i) $\nu = 1$, $\chi^2 = 3$, differences not significant, no definite improvement.
(ii) $\nu = 1$, $\chi^2 = 6 \cdot 6$, differences significant, definite improvement.

2. No. $\chi^2 = 3 \cdot 2$, differences not significant.

3. No. $\chi^2 = 3 \cdot 5$, differences not significant.

§78. 1. $\chi^2 = 0 \cdot 04$, no association exists.

2. $\chi^2 = 13 \cdot 1$, association exists.

§79. 1. $\chi^2 \doteqdot 119$. There was association.

2. $\chi^2 = 9 \cdot 9$. Association does exist. Different mortality rates are associated with different types of anaesthetic.

3. No. $\chi^2 = 2 \cdot 5$. Association does not exist.

4. Yes. $\chi^2 \doteqdot 15$. Association does exist.

5. Yes. $\chi^2 = 56$. High degree of association exists.

§81. 1. $\nu = 4$, $\chi^2 = 4 \cdot 9$, no association.

2. $\nu = 6$, $\chi^2 = 48 \cdot 3$, very definite association.

3. E's are 98, 146, 140, 103, 186, 280, 266, 200, 54, 82, 78, 56; $\nu = 6$, $\chi^2 = 162$, high degree of association.

§84. 1. $16 \cdot 40$ oz., $0 \cdot 311$ oz. 2. $0 \cdot 245$ in., $0 \cdot 0303$ in.

§88. 1. (a) $16 \cdot 40 \pm 0 \cdot 39$ oz.; (b) $\frac{9}{10}$ approx.

2. (a) $0 \cdot 245 \pm 0 \cdot 046$ in.; (b) (i) $\frac{1}{4}$ approx.; (ii) $\frac{1}{8}$ approx.

3. $507 \cdot 3 \pm 0 \cdot 96$; 1460.

§91. 1. Yes; $t = 2 \cdot 36$. 2. No; $t = 1 \cdot 77$. 3. No. $t = 1 \cdot 67$.

§93. 1. $\nu = 9$, $t = 1 \cdot 16$, difference not significant.

2. $\nu = 11$, $t = 2 \cdot 79$, difference is significant. The machine is set high.

§98. **1.** 13·70, 0·5093.   **2.** 3 min. 49 sec., 2·015 sec.; 0·0236.

     3. 0·06, 0·0384; 79·2 %.

§103. **1.** $t = 2·6$; significant at 5 % level but not at 1 % level.

     2. $t = 2·12$; difference is significant. Also the standard deviations prove that the thickness is nowhere less than 0·2 in.

§106. **1.** $m_1 = 11·88$, $s_1^2 = 53·5$; $m_2 = 13·08$, $s_2^2 = 66·5$.   S.E. $= 0·25$, $t = 0·48$, difference not significant.

     2. By the mean of the differences, $\nu = 9$, $t = 2·2$ slightly less than $P = 5 \%$ value. Improvement very doubtful. By difference of means $\nu = 18$, $t = 0·82$. Improvement not at all significant.

     3. A: $t = 3·58 > P = 1 \%$ value; significant (reads high). B: $t = 3·36 > P = 1 \%$ value; significant (reads low).

     4. $\nu = 10$, $t = 2·39 > P = 5 \%$ value. Significant. Experiment would be sounder using method of matched pairs of chickens.

     5. $\nu = 13$, $t = 4·29 > P = 0·1 \%$ value. Highly significant. The control group had higher ability in the first place. Improvement probably would be more difficult for them.

     6. $\nu = 5$, $t = 2·325 < P = 5 \%$ value. Difference not significant.

     7. $\nu = 10$, $t = 0·64$. No significant difference. A: $\nu = 5$, $t = 1·82$. Not significantly below 1000. B: $\nu = 5$, $t = 1·9$. Not significantly below 1000.

§113. (l) 10·86; (ii) 5·9; (iii) $10·86 \pm 2·22$; (iv) $10·86 \pm 3·50$. Under control after 1 week; out of control after 4 weeks.

§115. 97·5 % zone 10·7; 99·9 % zone 13·8. Two elevens indicate that control is doubtful after 1 week. 14, 12, 13, 15 indicate production completely out of control after 4 weeks.

§117. Allowable width 95·3 to 104·7 (i.e. 5·3 to 14·7 above 90). (i) Satisfactory after 1 week; (ii) not satisfactory after 4 weeks.

§119. $m = 1·5$; $c = 4$; as these are 4 *or more* 3 times out of 40 production is under control with a process average of $7\frac{1}{2} \%$ defective.

§130. **1.** $x = -1·14y + 89$. $y = -0·75x + 75$.

     2. $x = 1·54y + 1·53$.   **3.** $y = 40x - 8·4$.
     12·3 %; 10·75 across, 11·4 along.

     4. $r = 2·135$, $R = 0·055$.   **5.** $y = 54·9 + 0·5x$.

     6. $y = 0·216x - 9·25$, 0 is farthest above the line.

     8. $y = 109·5 + 2·716x - 0·183x^2$. $dy/dx = 0$ when $x = 7·5$.

§135. **1.** -0.76.   **2.** -0.93.   **3.** 0.86.   **4.** 0.82.

      5. 0.83.   **6.** 0.91; $y = 0.9x + 2$.   (i) 24.5; (ii) 42.5;

      7. 0.66. $y = 0.39x + 57$; £252.   (iii) 60.5.

§140. **1.** 0.78.   **2.** 0.62.   **3.** -0.95.

      4. 0.81.   **5.** 0.80.   **6.** 0.82.

Miscellaneous Problems

1. 14.05, 14.24; 0.86, 0.87 (in. Hg.). 0.85, 0.86 using Sheppard's correction.

2. A: 3, 5, 11, 17, 21, 22, 18, 12, 7, 3, 1.
    B: 2, 4, 8, 14, 20, 22, 20, 15, 9, 4, 2.

3. A: $\chi^2 = 9.47$, $\nu = 5$; not significant at 5 % level.
    B: $\chi^2 = 12.58$, $\nu = 4$; significant at 2.5 % level.

4. 14.05 ± 1.69 (in. Hg.).   **5.** $t = 1.7$; significant at 9 % level.

6. (i) $\frac{5}{16}$; (ii) $\frac{25}{32}$.   **7.** $\frac{3}{4}$.   **8.** (i) $\frac{60}{119}$; (iii) $\frac{741}{2728}$.

9. $s = 3.718$, $t = 1.99$, $\nu = 12$. Significant at 10 % level, but not at 5 % level.

10. (i) $4^4 e^{-4}/4! = 0.1952$; (ii) 0.6283.   **11.** $y = 4.15x + 2.32$.

12. $t = \sqrt{10}$. Significant 4.56 %.

13. (i) $e^{-0.5} = 0.6065$; (ii) $e^{-3} = 0.0498$.

14. $a = 1.32$, $b = -0.316$.   **15.** $\chi^2 = 1.71$, $\nu = 1$; not significant.

18. $a = -0.9$, $b = 13$.   **19.** (i) 0.097; (ii) 0.979.

20. $a = 2.3$, $b = -1.79$.   **22.** £636; £103.4.

23. $m = -2.66$, $c = 16.45$.   **24.** $a = 18.92$, $b = 0.38$, $c = 20$; 55.

25. (i) 7.44; (ii) 0.30.   **26.** 4, 1.789.

27. $20/\pi$; 6.2, $\pi = 3.23$.   **28.** $A = 60$, $\bar{x} = \frac{3}{7}$, $\sigma^2 = \frac{3}{98}$.

29. $A = \frac{15}{1024}$, $\bar{x} = 2\frac{2}{7}$, $\sigma = 2\sqrt{6}/7$.   **30.** $A = 2.314$, $\bar{x} = 0.343$, $\sigma = 0.418$.

31. $A = \frac{3}{64}$, $a = 4$; 0.138, 2.143.   **32.** a^2; $\bar{x} = 2a$, $\sigma = a\sqrt{2}$.

33. $\bar{y} = 2\frac{1}{3}$, $\sigma^2 = \frac{34}{45}$.   **34.** $\bar{y} = 468\frac{3}{4}$, $\sigma^2 = 0.6375$.

35. $\bar{y} = 7\pi/3$, $\sigma^2 = 34\pi^2/45$.   **36.** $\sqrt{\{(n^2-1)/12\}}$.

37. $(2n+1)/3$.   **38.** $\frac{106}{1024}$, $\frac{1981}{2048}$.

39. $\sqrt{\dfrac{2}{\pi}} = 0.8$.   **40.** $\dfrac{3}{2\pi}(2 - \sqrt{3})$;

$$\frac{1}{16\pi^2}(2\pi^2 - 3\sqrt{3}\pi - 252 + 144\sqrt{3}) = 0.0013.$$

41. 2 hr. 45 min., 5·385 min.; (i) 0·0316, 0·0004.

42. (i) 0·75; (ii) $y = 6·63x - 42·9$.

43. (i) 28; (ii) 38; (iii) 23; (iv) 11.　　　　**45.** 92; (i) $\frac{7}{15}$; (ii) $\frac{8}{15}$.

46. (i) 32·55, 4·682; (ii) 31·67, 5·105. $t = 2·065$; significant.

47. 2, 7·1; $t = 1·26$, not significant. 1·9, 3·2; $t = 2·66$, significant.

48. $a\bar{x} + b$, as. $y = 10(x/7 - 1)$.　　　**49.** $\frac{1}{10}\pi$; 2·5, $1\frac{2}{3}$, $3\frac{1}{3}$.

50. (i) $\frac{899}{1683}$; (ii) $\frac{4495}{11781}$; (iii) $\frac{331}{3927}$.

Glossary of Terms used
in this Work

Bernoulli's theorem. The theorem of which the binomial distribution is a corollary. If the probability of an event occurring at a single trial is p, the probability of exactly r occurrences of the event in n independent trials is $\binom{n}{r} p^r(1-p)^{n-r}$.

Binomial distribution. Suppose that the probability of an event occurring at a single trial is p and the probability of it not occurring is q then $p+q = 1$ and the probabilities

$$P(0), P(1), P(2), ..., P(r), ..., P(n)$$

of $0, 1, 2, ..., r, ..., n$ occurrences of the event in n independent trials are given by the terms of the *binomial expansion*

$$(q+p)^n = q^n + \binom{n}{1} q^{n-1}p + \binom{n}{2} q^{n-2}p^2 + ... + \binom{n}{r} q^{n-r}p^r + ... + p^n.$$

Chi-squared. $\chi^2 = \Sigma\left[\dfrac{(O-E)^2}{E}\right]$,

where O is the observed frequency of a particular class and E is the corresponding expected frequency.

Coefficient of correlation.

$$r_{xy} = \frac{\text{Covariance}}{\text{Product of standard deviations}} = \frac{s_{xy}}{s_x s_y}.$$

Coefficient of rank correlation (Spearman's).

$$R = 1 - \frac{6\Sigma D^2}{n(n^2-1)}.$$

Coefficient of regression. The gradient of the regression line.
The coefficient of regression of y on x is s_{xy}/s_x^2.
The coefficient of regression of x on y is s_{xy}/s_y^2.

Combinations (or selections) $\binom{n}{r}$ or ^nC_r. The number of combinations of n unlike things taken r at a time is

$$\binom{n}{r} = \frac{n(n-1)(n-2) ... (n-r+1)}{1.2.3 ... r} = \frac{n!}{r!(n-r)!}.$$

GLOSSARY

Compound probability. If the probabilities of several independent events are $p_1, p_2, \ldots, p_n$, the probability that *all* will take place is the *product* $p_1 p_2 \ldots p_n$.

Confidence limits of the mean. The 95 % confidence limits of the mean are $m \pm \dfrac{ts}{\sqrt{n}}$, where t is the $P = 5\%$ value of the t-distribution for $\nu = n-1$ (sample of size n). Similarly the 99·8 % confidence limits are obtained from the $P = 0·2\%$ value. The probability that the true mean lies outside the 95 % confidence limits is 5 % or $\frac{1}{20}$.

Covariance of a bivariate distribution.

For n separate (x, y) pairs

$$s_{xy} = \frac{1}{n} \Sigma(x-\overline{x})(y-\overline{y})$$

$$= \frac{\Sigma xy}{n} - \left(\frac{\Sigma x}{n}\right)\left(\frac{\Sigma y}{n}\right).$$

For a grouped distribution

$$s_{xy} = \frac{\Sigma fxy}{\Sigma f} - \left(\frac{\Sigma f_x x}{\Sigma f}\right)\left(\frac{\Sigma f_y y}{\Sigma f}\right).$$

Degrees of freedom. In calculating the standard deviation of n observations the sum of the deviations from the mean is zero. Hence, when $(n-1)$ deviations have been written down, the nth deviation is determined and we say that for n observations there are $(n-1)$ degrees of freedom. See also table A3, page 142.

Least squares line of best fit. If $y = ax+b$ is the equation the values of a and b are given by the *normal* equations

$$\Sigma y = a\Sigma x + nb,$$

$$\Sigma xy = a\Sigma x^2 + b\Sigma x,$$

where n is the number of (x, y) pairs.

An alternative form of the equation is

$$(y-\overline{y}) = \frac{s_{xy}}{s_x^2}(x-\overline{x})$$

or

$$(y-\overline{y}) = \frac{r_{xy} \cdot s_y}{s_x}(x-\overline{x}).$$

Level of significance. See 'Significance'.

Lower quartile. The lower quartile divides the area under the probability curve (not necessarily 'normal') in the ratio $1:3$. The lower quartile is the 25th percentile.

Mean. The arithmetic mean, or more simply the mean, of the n values $x_1, x_2, \ldots, x_n$ is

$$\overline{x} = \frac{1}{n}(x_1 + x_2 + \ldots + x_n)$$

$$= \frac{1}{n}\Sigma x.$$

If the n values have respective frequencies $f_1, f_2, ..., f_n$

$$\bar{x} = \frac{f_1 x_1 + f_2 x_2 + ... + f_n x_n}{f_1 + f_2 + ... + f_n}$$
$$= \Sigma fx / \Sigma f.$$

For a *continuous probability curve* $y = f(x)$, $(a \leqslant x \leqslant b)$,

$$\bar{x} = \int_a^b xy\,dx \Big/ \int_a^b y\,dx.$$

$\left(\text{Usually } \int_a^b y\,dx = 1 \text{ and } \bar{x} = \int_a^b xy\,dx.\right)$

Mean deviation. The mean deviation of the n values $x_1, x_2, ..., x_n$ is

$$\frac{1}{n}\{|x_1 - \bar{x}| + |x_2 - \bar{x}| + ... + |x_n - \bar{x}|\} = \frac{1}{n}\Sigma|x - \bar{x}|.$$

If the n values have respective frequencies $f_1, f_2, ..., f_n$ the mean deviation

$$= \frac{f_1|x_1 - \bar{x}| + f_2|x_2 - \bar{x}| + ... + f_n|x_n - \bar{x}|}{f_1 + f_2 + ... + f_n}$$
$$= \Sigma f|x - \bar{x}| / \Sigma f.$$

For a *continuous probability curve* $y = f(x)$, $(a \leqslant x \leqslant b)$, mean deviation $= \int_a^b |x - \bar{x}|\, y\,dx \Big/ \int_a^b y\,dx.$

Median. The median bisects the area under the probability curve (not necessarily 'normal'). The median is the 50th percentile.

Normal equations. See 'Least squares line of best fit'.

Normal frequency curve. The equation of the normal frequency curve in its most general form is

$$y = \frac{1}{\sigma\sqrt{(2\pi)}}\, e^{-\frac{1}{2}(x-\mu)^2/\sigma^2}.$$

Here, μ is the mean and σ the standard deviation and the distribution is known as *normal* (μ, σ). Table A1, page 139, gives values of the normal $(0, 1)$ distribution.

Null hypothesis. The null hypothesis is the *assumption* which is made when applying a significance test.

Parameters. A collective name given to statistical measures such as the mean and standard deviation.

Percentiles. The values which divide the area under the probability curve (not necessarily 'normal') into a hundred equal parts. The 25th, 50th and 75th percentiles are known as the lower quartile, median and upper quartile respectively.

Poisson distribution. The Poisson distribution is the form assumed by the binomial distribution when p is small and n is large, the mean number of occurrences np being a finite constant a. In this case the probabilities $P(0), P(1), P(2), ..., P(r)$ of $0, 1, 2, ..., r$ occurrences of the event are

$$e^{-a}, ae^{-a}, \frac{a^2}{2!}e^{-a}, ... \frac{a^r}{r!}e^{-a}$$

respectively.

Quartiles. See 'Lower quartile' and 'Upper quartile'.

Selections. See 'Combinations'.

Sheppard's correction for grouping. When the mean and variance are calculated from a grouped frequency distribution such as that of table 6A, page 43, errors occur because each observation in a group takes the mid-value of the group. The final error in the mean is negligible because the positive and negative errors in the individual observations tend to cancel each other. In the calculation of the variance, however, all the terms are positive due to squaring. An allowance can be made for the error thus caused by grouping. It is to *reduce the variance by* $\dfrac{c^2}{12}$ *where c is the length of the class interval*. This is known as Sheppard's correction. The formula for the standard deviation thus becomes

$$s = \sqrt{\left\{\frac{\Sigma fx^2}{\Sigma f} - \left(\frac{\Sigma fx}{\Sigma f}\right)^2 - \frac{c^2}{12}\right\}}.$$

It will be realized that 'working units' are often chosen so that $c = 1$.

Significance. The level of significance is the probability that the null hypothesis is true.

Significance of a single mean. Compare $t = \dfrac{|\mu - m|}{s/\sqrt{n}}$ with the percentage points of the t-distribution given in table A5 ($\nu = n-1$).

Significance of the difference between means.

For large samples $t = \dfrac{|m_1 - m_2|}{\sqrt{\left(\dfrac{s_1^2}{n_1} + \dfrac{s_2^2}{n_2}\right)}}.$

For small samples $t = \dfrac{|m_1 - m_2|}{s\sqrt{\left(\dfrac{1}{n_1} + \dfrac{1}{n_2}\right)}},$ where $s^2 = \dfrac{(n_1 - 1)\,s_1^2 + (n_2 - 1)\,s_2^2}{(n_1 + n_2 - 2)}.$

Compare t with the percentage points given in table A5 taking

$$\nu = n_1 + n_2 - 2.$$

Standard deviation. The standard deviation of the n values $x_1, x_2, \dots x_n$ is

$$s = \sqrt{\left\{\frac{\Sigma(x - \bar{x})^2}{n}\right\}}$$

$$= \sqrt{\left\{\frac{\Sigma x^2}{n} - \left(\frac{\Sigma x}{n}\right)^2\right\}} \quad \text{if } n \text{ is large,}$$

or $s = \sqrt{\left\{\frac{\Sigma(x - \bar{x})^2}{(n-1)}\right\}}$

$$= \sqrt{\left\{\frac{\Sigma x^2}{(n-1)} - \frac{n}{(n-1)}\left(\frac{\Sigma x}{n}\right)^2\right\}} \quad \text{if } n \text{ is small.}$$

If the n values have respective frequencies $f_1, f_2, \dots, f_n$

$$s = \sqrt{\left\{\frac{\Sigma f(x - \bar{x})^2}{\Sigma f}\right\}}$$

$$= \sqrt{\left\{\frac{\Sigma fx^2}{\Sigma f} - \left(\frac{\Sigma fx}{\Sigma f}\right)^2\right\}}.$$

For a continuous probability curve $y = f(x)$, $(a \leqslant x \leqslant b)$, for which $\int_a^b y\,dx = 1$

$$s = \sqrt{\left\{ \int_a^b x^2 y\,dx - \left(\int_a^b xy\,dx \right)^2 \right\}}.$$

Standardized deviate. The standardized deviate of a value x is $\dfrac{(x-\bar{x})}{s}$.

Upper quartile. The upper quartile divides the area under the probability curve (not necessarily 'normal') in the ratio $3:1$. The upper quartile is the 75th percentile.

Yates's correction for continuity. In the calculation of χ^2, if $\nu = 1$ the $(O - E)$ differences must each be diminished numerically by $\frac{1}{2}$.

Index

Appendix

Tables A1, 2, 4, 5. Reprinted from Lindley and Miller, *Cambridge Elementary Statistical Tables*.
Table A6. The e^{-x} table is taken from Godfrey and Siddons, *Four-Figure Tables*.
Logarithms, Antilogarithms, Squares and Square-roots are reprinted from *The Cambridge Four-Figure Mathematical Tables*.

TABLE AI

x	y	x	y	x	y	x	y
0·0	0·3989	1·0	0·2420	2·0	0·0540	3·0	0·0044
·1	·3970	·1	·2179	·1	·0440	·1	·0033
·2	·3910	·2	·1942	·2	·0355	·2	·0024
·3	·3814	·3	·1714	·3	·0283	·3	·0017
·4	·3683	·4	·1497	·4	·0224	·4	·0012
0·5	0·3521	1·5	0·1295	2·5	0·0175	3·5	0·0009
·6	·3332	·6	·1109	·6	·0136	·6	·0006
·7	·3123	·7	·0940	·7	·0104	·7	·0004
·8	·2897	·8	·0790	·8	·0079	·8	·0003
·9	·2661	·9	·0656	·9	·0060	·9	·0002
1·0	0·2420	2·0	0·0540	3·0	0·0044	4·0	0·0001

Values of the ordinate $y = \dfrac{1}{\sqrt{(2\pi)}} e^{-\frac{1}{2}x^2}$ of the normal probability curve.

TABLE A 2

x	A(x)		x	A(x)		x	A(x)		x	A(x)		x	A(x)		x	A(x)		x	A(x)
0·00	0·5000 40		0·50	0·6915 35		1·00	0·8413 25		1·50	0·9332 13		2·00	0·97725 53		2·50	0·99379 17		2·90	0·99813 6
·01	·5040 40		·51	·6950 35		·01	·8438 23		·51	·9345 12		·01	·97778 53		·51	·99396 17		·91	·99819 6
·02	·5080 40		·52	·6985 34		·02	·8461 24		·52	·9357 13		·02	·97831 51		·52	·99413 17		·92	·99825 6
·03	·5120 40		·53	·7019 35		·03	·8485 23		·53	·9370 12		·03	·97882 50		·53	·99430 16		·93	·99831 5
·04	·5160 39		·54	·7054 34		·04	·8508 23		·54	·9382 12		·04	·97932 50		·54	·99446 15		·94	·99836 5
0·05	·5199 40		0·55	0·7088 35		1·05	0·8531 23		1·55	0·9394 12		2·05	0·97982 48		2·55	0·99461 16		2·95	0·99841 5
·06	·5239 40		·56	·7123 34		·06	·8554 23		·56	·9406 12		·06	·98030 47		·56	·99477 15		·96	·99846 5
·07	·5279 40		·57	·7157 33		·07	·8577 22		·57	·9418 11		·07	·98077 47		·57	·99492 14		·97	·99851 5
·08	·5319 40		·58	·7190 34		·08	·8599 22		·58	·9429 12		·08	·98124 45		·58	·99506 14		·98	·99856 5
·09	·5359 39		·59	·7224 33		·09	·8621 22		·59	·9441 11		·09	·98169 45		·59	·99520 14		·99	·99861 4
0·10	0·5398 40		0·60	0·7257 34		1·10	0·8643 22		1·60	0·9452 11		2·10	0·98214 43		2·60	0·99534 13		3·0	0·99865 38
·11	·5438 40		·61	·7291 33		·11	·8665 21		·61	·9463 11		·11	·98257 43		·61	·99547 13		3·1	·99903 28
·12	·5478 39		·62	·7324 33		·12	·8686 22		·62	·9474 10		·12	·98300 41		·62	·99560 13		3·2	·99931 21
·13	·5517 40		·63	·7357 32		·13	·8708 21		·63	·9484 11		·13	·98341 41		·63	·99573 12		3·3	·99952 14
·14	·5557 39		·64	·7389 33		·14	·8729 20		·64	·9495 10		·14	·98382 40		·64	·99585 13		3·4	·99966 11
0·15	0·5596 40		0·65	0·7422 32		1·15	0·8749 21		1·65	0·9505 10		2·15	0·98422 39		2·65	0·99598 11		3·5	0·99977 7
·16	·5636 39		·66	·7454 32		·16	·8770 20		·66	·9515 10		·16	·98461 39		·66	·99609 12		3·6	·99984 5
·17	·5675 39		·67	·7486 31		·17	·8790 20		·67	·9525 10		·17	·98500 37		·67	·99621 11		3·7	·99989 4
·18	·5714 39		·68	·7517 32		·18	·8810 20		·68	·9535 10		·18	·98537 37		·68	·99632 11		3·8	·99993 2
·19	·5753 40		·69	·7549 31		·19	·8830 19		·69	·9545 9		·19	·98574 36		·69	·99643 10		3·9	·99995 2
0·20	0·5793 39		0·70	0·7580 31		1·20	0·8849 20		1·70	0·9554 10		2·20	0·98610 35		2·70	0·99653 11		4·0	0·99997
·21	·5832 39		·71	·7611 31		·21	·8869 19		·71	·9564 9		·21	·98645 34		·71	·99664 10			
·22	·5871 39		·72	·7642 31		·22	·8888 19		·72	·9573 9		·22	·98679 34		·72	·99674 9			
·23	·5910 38		·73	·7673 31		·23	·8907 18		·73	·9582 9		·23	·98713 32		·73	·99683 10			
·24	·5948 39		·74	·7704 30		·24	·8925 19		·74	·9591 8		·24	·98745 33		·74	·99693 9			

x	A(x)		x	A(x)		x	A(x)		x	A(x)		x	A(x)		x	A(x)	
0·25	0·5987	39	0·75	0·7734	30	1·25	0·8944	18	1·75	0·9599	9	2·25	0·98778	31	2·75	0·99702	9
·26	·6026	38	·76	·7764	30	·26	·8962	18	·76	·9608	8	·26	·98809	31	·76	·99711	9
·27	·6064	39	·77	·7794	29	·27	·8980	17	·77	·9616	9	·27	·98840	30	·77	·99720	8
·28	·6103	38	·78	·7823	29	·28	·8997	18	·78	·9625	8	·28	·98870	29	·78	·99728	8
·29	·6141	38	·79	·7852	29	·29	·9015	17	·79	·9633	8	·29	·98899	29	·79	·99736	8
0·30	0·6179	38	0·80	0·7881	29	1·30	0·9032	17	1·80	0·9641	8	2·30	0·98928	28	2·80	0·99744	8
·31	·6217	38	·81	·7910	29	·31	·9049	17	·81	·9649	7	·31	·98956	27	·81	·99752	8
·32	·6255	38	·82	·7939	28	·32	·9066	16	·82	·9656	8	·32	·98983	27	·82	·99760	7
·33	·6293	38	·83	·7967	28	·33	·9082	17	·83	·9664	7	·33	·99010	26	·83	·99767	7
·34	·6331	37	·84	·7995	28	·34	·9099	16	·84	·9671	7	·34	·99036	25	·84	·99774	7
0·35	0·6368	38	0·85	0·8023	28	1·35	0·9115	16	1·85	0·9678	8	2·35	0·99061	25	2·85	0·99781	7
·36	·6406	37	·86	·8051	27	·36	·9131	16	·86	·9686	7	·36	·99086	25	·86	·99788	7
·37	·6443	37	·87	·8078	28	·37	·9147	15	·87	·9693	6	·37	·99111	23	·87	·99795	6
·38	·6480	37	·88	·8106	27	·38	·9162	15	·88	·9699	7	·38	·99134	24	·88	·99801	6
·39	·6517	37	·89	·8133	26	·39	·9177	15	·89	·9706	7	·39	·99158	22	·89	·99807	6
0·40	0·6554	37	0·90	0·8159	27	1·40	0·9192	15	1·90	0·9713	6	2·40	0·99180	22	2·90	0·99813	
·41	·6591	37	·91	·8186	26	·41	·9207	15	·91	·9719	7	·41	·99202	22			
·42	·6628	36	·92	·8212	26	·42	·9222	14	·92	·9726	6	·42	·99224	21			
·43	·6664	36	·93	·8238	26	·43	·9236	15	·93	·9732	6	·43	·99245	21			
·44	·6700	36	·94	·8264	25	·44	·9251	14	·94	·9738	6	·44	·99266	20			
0·45	0·6736	36	0·95	0·8289	26	1·45	0·9265	14	1·95	0·9744	6	2·45	0·99286	19			
·46	·6772	36	·96	·8315	25	·46	·9279	13	·96	·9750	6	·46	·99305	19			
·47	·6808	36	·97	·8340	25	·47	·9292	14	·97	·9756	5	·47	·99324	19			
·48	·6844	35	·98	·8365	24	·48	·9306	13	·98	·9761	6	·48	·99343	18			
·49	·6879	36	·99	·8389	24	·49	·9319	13	·99	·9767	5	·49	·99361	18			
0·50	0·6915	36	1·00	0·8413		1·50	0·9332		2·00	0·9772		2·50	0·99379				

The function tabulated above is the total area $A(x)$ under the normal probability curve to the left of a given value of x. Mathematically it is stated as

$$A(x) = \frac{1}{\sqrt{(2\pi)}} \int_{-\infty}^{x} e^{-\frac{1}{2}t^2}\, dt.$$

APPENDIX

TABLE A3

*Rules for determining the number of degrees of freedom, v,
when applying the χ^2-test*

Test of	Restrictions	No. of degrees of freedom v
Normal distribution	Means Standard deviations $\Big\}$ agree Totals	(No. of classes -3)
Binomial distribution	(a) If p is given Totals agree	(No. of classes -1)
	(b) If p has to be determined from the data Means $\Big\}$ agree Totals	(No. of classes -2)
Poisson distribution	Means $\Big\}$ agree Totals	(No. of classes -2)
$1 \times k$ Contingency table	Totals agree	$(k-1)$
$h \times k$ Contingency table	h row totals agree k column totals agree	$(h-1)(k-1)$

TABLE A4
Percentage points of the χ^2-distribution

P	99·5	99	97·5	95	10	5	2·5	1	0·5	0·1
$\nu = 1$	0.0^4393	0.0^3157	0.0^3982	0·00393	2·71	3·84	5·02	6·63	7·88	10·83
2	0·0100	0·0201	0·0506	0·103	4·61	5·99	7·38	9·21	10·60	13·81
3	0·0717	0·115	0·216	0·352	6·25	7·81	9·35	11·34	12·84	16·27
4	0·207	0·297	0·484	0·711	7·78	9·49	11·14	13·28	14·86	18·47
5	0·412	0·554	0·831	1·15	9·24	11·07	12·83	15·09	16·75	20·52
6	0·676	0·872	1·24	1·64	10·64	12·59	14·45	16·81	18·55	22·46
7	0·989	1·24	1·69	2·17	12·02	14·07	16·01	18·48	20·28	24·32
8	1·34	1·65	2·18	2·73	13·36	15·51	17·53	20·09	21·95	26·12
9	1·73	2·09	2·70	3·33	14·68	16·92	19·02	21·67	23·59	27·88
10	2·16	2·56	3·25	3·94	15·99	18·31	20·48	23·21	25·19	29·59
11	2·60	3·05	3·82	4·57	17·28	19·68	21·92	24·73	26·76	31·26
12	3·07	3·57	4·40	5·23	18·55	21·03	23·34	26·22	28·30	32·91
13	3·57	4·11	5·01	5·89	19·81	22·36	24·74	27·69	29·82	34·53
14	4·07	4·66	5·63	6·57	21·06	23·68	26·12	29·14	31·32	36·12
15	4·60	5·23	6·26	7·26	22·31	25·00	27·49	30·58	32·80	37·70
16	5·14	5·81	6·91	7·96	23·54	26·30	28·85	32·00	34·27	39·25
17	5·70	6·41	7·56	8·67	24·77	27·59	30·19	33·41	35·72	40·79
18	6·26	7·01	8·23	9·39	25·99	28·87	31·53	34·81	37·16	42·31
19	6·84	7·63	8·91	10·12	27·20	30·14	32·85	36·19	38·58	43·82
20	7·43	8·26	9·59	10·85	28·41	31·41	34·17	37·57	40·00	45·31
21	8·03	8·90	10·28	11·59	29·62	32·67	35·48	38·93	41·40	46·80
22	8·64	9·54	10·98	12·34	30·81	33·92	36·78	40·29	42·80	48·27
23	9·26	10·20	11·69	13·09	32·01	35·17	38·08	41·64	44·18	49·73
24	9·89	10·86	12·40	13·85	33·20	36·42	39·36	42·98	45·56	51·18
25	10·52	11·52	13·12	14·61	34·38	37·65	40·65	44·31	46·93	52·62
26	11·16	12·20	13·84	15·38	35·56	38·89	41·92	45·64	48·29	54·05
27	11·81	12·88	14·57	16·15	36·74	40·11	43·19	46·96	49·64	55·48
28	12·46	13·56	15·31	16·93	37·92	41·34	44·46	48·28	50·99	56·89
29	13·12	14·26	16·05	17·71	39·09	42·56	45·72	49·59	52·34	58·30
30	13·79	14·95	16·79	18·49	40·26	43·77	46·98	50·89	53·67	59·70
40	20·71	22·16	24·43	26·51	51·81	55·76	59·34	63·69	66·77	73·40
50	27·99	29·71	32·36	34·76	63·17	67·50	71·42	76·15	79·49	86·66
60	35·53	37·48	40·48	43·19	74·40	79·08	83·30	88·38	91·95	99·61
70	43·28	45·44	48·76	51·74	85·53	90·53	95·02	100·4	104·2	112·3
80	51·17	53·54	57·15	60·39	96·58	101·9	106·6	112·3	116·3	124·8
90	59·20	61·75	65·65	69·13	107·6	113·1	118·1	124·1	128·3	137·2
100	67·33	70·06	74·22	77·93	118·5	124·3	129·6	135·8	140·2	149·4

The function tabulated is χ_P^2 defined by the equation $\dfrac{P}{100} = \dfrac{1}{2^{\nu/1}\Gamma(\frac{1}{2}\nu)} \displaystyle\int_{x_P^2}^{\infty} x^{\frac{1}{2}\nu-1}\, e^{-x/2} dx$. If x is a variable distributed as χ^2 with ν degrees of freedom, $P/100$ is the probability that $x \geqslant \chi_P^2$. For $\nu < 100$, linear interpolation in ν is adequate. For $\nu > 100$, $\sqrt{(2\chi^2)}$ is approximately normally distributed with mean $\sqrt{(2\nu - 1)}$ and unit variance, and the percentage points may be obtained from table A2.

TABLE A5
Percentage points of the t-distribution

P	25	10	5	2	1	0·2	0·1	$\frac{120}{\nu}$
$\nu = 1$	2·41	6·31	12·71	31·82	63·66	318·3	636·6	
2	1·60	2·92	4·30	6·96	9·92	22·33	31·60	
3	1·42	2·35	3·18	4·54	5·84	10·21	12·92	
4	1·34	2·13	2·78	3·75	4·60	7·17	8·61	
5	1·30	2·02	2·57	3·36	4·03	5·89	6·87	
6	1·27	1·94	2·45	3·14	3·71	5·21	5·96	
7	1·25	1·89	2·36	3·00	3·50	4·79	5·41	
8	1·24	1·86	2·31	2·90	3·36	4·50	5·04	
9	1·23	1·83	2·26	2·82	3·25	4·30	4·78	
10	1·22	1·81	2·23	2·76	3·17	4·14	4·59	12
12	1·21	1·78	2·18	2·68	3·05	3·93	4·32	10
15	1·20	1·75	2·13	2·60	2·95	3·73	4·07	8
20	1·18	1·72	2·09	2·53	2·85	3·55	3·85	6
24	1·18	1·71	2·06	2·49	2·80	3·47	3·75	5
30	1·17	1·70	2·04	2·46	2·75	3·39	3·65	4
40	1·17	1·68	2·02	2·42	2·70	3·31	3·55	3
60	1·16	1·67	2·00	2·39	2·66	3·23	3·46	2
120	1·16	1·66	1·98	2·36	2·62	3·16	3·37	1
∞	1·15	1·64	1·96	2·33	2·58	3·09	3·29	0

The function tabulated is t_P defined by the equation

$$\frac{P}{100} = \frac{1}{\sqrt{(\nu\pi)}} \frac{\Gamma(\frac{1}{2}\nu + \frac{1}{2})}{\Gamma(\frac{1}{2}\nu)} \int_{|t| \geqslant t_P} \frac{dt}{(1 + t^2/\nu)^{\frac{1}{2}(\nu+1)}}.$$

If t is the ratio of a random variable, normally distributed with zero mean, to an independent estimate of its standard deviation based on ν degrees of freedom, $P/100$ is the probability that $|t| \geqslant t_P$.

Interpolation ν-wise should be linear in $120/\nu$.

Other percentage points may be found approximately, except when ν and P are both small, by using the fact that the variable

$$y = \pm \sinh^{-1}\{\sqrt{(3t^2/2\nu)}\},$$

where y has the same sign as t, is approximately normally distributed with zero mean and variance $3/(2\nu - 1)$.

TABLE A6

e^{-x} (*for use with the Poisson distribution*)

x	·00	·01	·02	·03	·04	·05	·06	·07	·08	·09
0·0	1·0000	·9900	·9802	·9704	·9608	·9512	·9418	·9324	·9231	·9139
0·1	0·9048	·8958	·8869	·8781	·8694	·8607	·8521	·8437	·8353	·8270
·2	·8187	·8106	·8025	·7945	·7866	·7788	·7711	·7634	·7558	·7483
·3	·7408	·7334	·7261	·7189	·7118	·7047	·6977	·6907	·6839	·6771
·4	·6703	·6637	·6570	·6505	·6440	·6376	·6313	·6250	·6188	·6126
·5	·6065	·6005	·5945	·5886	·5827	·5769	·5712	·5655	·5599	·5543
·6	·5488	·5434	·5379	·5326	·5273	·5220	·5169	·5117	·5066	·5016
·7	·4966	·4916	·4868	·4819	·4771	·4724	·4677	·4630	·4584	·4538
·8	·4493	·4449	·4404	·4360	·4317	·4274	·4232	·4190	·4148	·4107
·9	·4066	·4025	·3985	·3946	·3906	·3867	·3829	·3791	·3753	·3716
1·0	0·3679	·3642	·3606	·3570	·3535	·3499	·3465	·3430	·3396	·3362
1·1	·3329	·3296	·3263	·3230	·3198	·3166	·3135	·3104	·3073	·3042
·2	·3012	·2982	·2952	·2923	·2894	·2865	·2837	·2808	·2780	·2753
·3	·2725	·2698	·2671	·2645	·2618	·2592	·2567	·2541	·2516	·2491
·4	·2466	·2441	·2417	·2393	·2369	·2346	·2322	·2299	·2276	·2254
·5	·2231	·2209	·2187	·2165	·2144	·2122	·2101	·2080	·2060	·2039
·6	·2019	·1999	·1979	·1959	·1940	·1920	·1901	·1882	·1864	·1845
·7	·1827	·1809	·1791	·1773	·1755	·1738	·1720	·1703	·1686	·1670
·8	·1653	·1637	·1620	·1604	·1588	·1572	·1557	·1541	·1526	·1511
·9	·1496	·1481	·1466	·1451	·1437	·1423	·1409	·1395	·1381	·1367
2·0	0·1353	·1340	·1327	·1313	·1300	·1287	·1275	·1262	·1249	·1237
2·1	0·1225	·1212	·1200	·1188	·1177	·1165	·1153	·1142	·1130	·1119
·2	·1108	·1097	·1086	·1075	·1065	·1054	·1044	·1033	·1023	·1013
·3	·1003	·0993	·0983	·0973	·0963	·0954	·0944	·0935	·0925	·0916
·4	·0907	·0898	·0889	·0880	·0872	·0863	·0854	·0846	·0837	·0829
·5	·0821	·0813	·0805	·0797	·0789	·0781	·0773	·0765	·0758	·0750
·6	·0743	·0735	·0728	·0721	·0714	·0707	·0699	·0693	·0686	·0679
·7	·0672	·0665	·0659	·0652	·0646	·0639	·0633	·0627	·0620	·0614
·8	·0608	·0602	·0596	·0590	·0584	·0578	·0573	·0567	·0561	·0556
·9	·0550	·0545	·0539	·0534	·0529	·0523	·0518	·0513	·0508	·0503
3·0	0·0498	·0493	·0488	·0483	·0478	·0474	·0469	·0464	·0460	·0455
3·1	·0450	·0446	·0442	·0437	·0433	·0429	·0424	·0420	·0416	·0412
·2	·0408	·0404	·0400	·0396	·0392	·0388	·0384	·0380	·0376	·0373
·3	·0369	·0365	·0362	·0358	·0354	·0351	·0347	·0344	·0340	·0337
·4	·0334	·0330	·0327	·0324	·0321	·0317	·0314	·0311	·0308	·0305
·5	·0302	·0299	·0296	·0293	·0290	·0287	·0284	·0282	·0279	·0276
·6	·0273	·0271	·0268	·0265	·0260	·0257	·0257	·0255	·0252	·0250
·7	·0247	·0245	·0242	·0240	·0238	·0235	·0233	·0231	·0228	·0226
·8	·0224	·0221	·0219	·0217	·0215	·0213	·0211	·0209	·0207	·0204
·9	·0202	·0200	·0198	·0196	·0194	·0193	·0191	·0189	·0187	·0185
4·0	0·0183									
x	·00	·01	·02	·03	·04	·05	·06	·07	·08	·−9

	0	1	2	3	4	5	6	7	8	9	Differences							
											1	2	3	4	5	6	7	8
10	0000	0043	0086	0128	0170	0212	0253	0294	0334	0374	4	8	12	17	21	25	29	33
11	0414	0453	0492	0531	0569	0607	0645	0682	0719	0755	4	8	11	15	19	23	26	30
12	0792	0828	0864	0899	0934	0969	1004	1038	1072	1106	3	7	10	14	17	21	24	28
13	1139	1173	1206	1239	1271	1303	1335	1367	1399	1430	3	6	10	13	16	19	23	26
14	1461	1492	1523	1553	1584	1614	1644	1673	1703	1732	3	6	9	12	15	18	21	24
15	1761	1790	1818	1847	1875	1903	1931	1959	1987	2014	3	6	8	11	14	17	20	22
16	2041	2068	2095	2122	2148	2175	2201	2227	2253	2279	3	5	8	11	13	16	18	21
17	2304	2330	2355	2380	2405	2430	2455	2480	2504	2529	2	5	7	10	12	15	17	20
18	2553	2577	2601	2625	2648	2672	2695	2718	2742	2765	2	5	7	9	12	14	16	19
19	2788	2810	2833	2856	2878	2900	2923	2945	2967	2989	2	4	7	9	11	13	16	18
20	3010	3032	3054	3075	3096	3118	3139	3160	3181	3201	2	4	6	8	11	13	15	17
21	3222	3243	3263	3284	3304	3324	3345	3365	3385	3404	2	4	6	8	10	12	14	16
22	3424	3444	3464	3483	3502	3522	3541	3560	3579	3598	2	4	6	8	10	12	14	15
23	3617	3636	3655	3674	3692	3711	3729	3747	3766	3784	2	4	6	7	9	11	13	15
24	3802	3820	3838	3856	3874	3892	3909	3927	3945	3962	2	4	5	7	9	11	12	14
25	3979	3997	4014	4031	4048	4065	4082	4099	4116	4133	2	3	5	7	9	10	12	14
26	4150	4166	4183	4200	4216	4232	4249	4265	4281	4298	2	3	5	7	8	10	11	13
27	4314	4330	4346	4362	4378	4393	4409	4425	4440	4456	2	3	5	6	8	9	11	13
28	4472	4487	4502	4518	4533	4548	4564	4579	4594	4609	2	3	5	6	8	9	11	12
29	4624	4639	4654	4669	4683	4698	4713	4728	4742	4757	1	3	4	6	7	9	10	12
30	4771	4786	4800	4814	4829	4843	4857	4871	4886	4900	1	3	4	6	7	9	10	11
31	4914	4928	4942	4955	4969	4983	4997	5011	5024	5038	1	3	4	6	7	8	10	11
32	5051	5065	5079	5092	5105	5119	5132	5145	5159	5172	1	3	4	5	7	8	9	11
33	5185	5198	5211	5224	5237	5250	5263	5276	5289	5302	1	3	4	5	6	8	9	10
34	5315	5328	5340	5353	5366	5378	5391	5403	5416	5428	1	3	4	5	6	8	9	10
35	5441	5453	5465	5478	5490	5502	5514	5527	5539	5551	1	2	4	5	6	7	9	10
36	5563	5575	5587	5599	5611	5623	5635	5647	5658	5670	1	2	4	5	6	7	8	10
37	5682	5694	5705	5717	5729	5740	5752	5763	5775	5786	1	2	3	5	6	7	8	9
38	5798	5809	5821	5832	5843	5855	5866	5877	5888	5899	1	2	3	5	6	7	8	9
39	5911	5922	5933	5944	5955	5966	5977	5988	5999	6010	1	2	3	4	5	7	8	9
40	6021	6031	6042	6053	6064	6075	6085	6096	6107	6117	1	2	3	4	5	6	8	9
41	6128	6138	6149	6160	6170	6180	6191	6201	6212	6222	1	2	3	4	5	6	7	8
42	6232	6243	6253	6263	6274	6284	6294	6304	6314	6325	1	2	3	4	5	6	7	8
43	6335	6345	6355	6365	6375	6385	6395	6405	6415	6425	1	2	3	4	5	6	7	8
44	6435	6444	6454	6464	6474	6484	6493	6503	6513	6522	1	2	3	4	5	6	7	8
45	6532	6542	6551	6561	6571	6580	6590	6599	6609	6618	1	2	3	4	5	6	7	8
46	6628	6637	6646	6656	6665	6675	6684	6693	6702	6712	1	2	3	4	5	6	7	7
47	6721	6730	6739	6749	6758	6767	6776	6785	6794	6803	1	2	3	4	5	5	6	7
48	6812	6821	6830	6839	6848	6857	6866	6875	6884	6893	1	2	3	4	4	5	6	7
49	6902	6911	6920	6928	6937	6946	6955	6964	6972	6981	1	2	3	4	4	5	6	7
50	6990	6998	7007	7016	7024	7033	7042	7050	7059	7067	1	2	3	3	4	5	6	7
51	7076	7084	7093	7101	7110	7118	7126	7135	7143	7152	1	2	3	3	4	5	6	7
52	7160	7168	7177	7185	7193	7202	7210	7218	7226	7235	1	2	2	3	4	5	6	7
53	7243	7251	7259	7267	7275	7284	7292	7300	7308	7316	1	2	2	3	4	5	6	6
54	7324	7332	7340	7348	7356	7364	7372	7380	7388	7396	1	2	2	3	4	5	6	6
	0	1	2	3	4	5	6	7	8	9	1	2	3	4	5	6	7	8

	0	1	2	3	4	5	6	7	8	9	Differences								
											1	2	3	4	5	6	7	8	9
5	7404	7412	7419	7427	7435	7443	7451	7459	7466	7474	1	2	2	3	4	5	5	6	7
6	7482	7490	7497	7505	7513	7520	7528	7536	7543	7551	1	2	2	3	4	5	5	6	7
7	7559	7566	7574	7582	7589	7597	7604	7612	7619	7627	1	2	2	3	4	5	5	6	7
8	7634	7642	7649	7657	7664	7672	7679	7686	7694	7701	1	1	2	3	4	4	5	6	7
9	7709	7716	7723	7731	7738	7745	7752	7760	7767	7774	1	1	2	3	4	4	5	6	7
0	7782	7789	7796	7803	7810	7818	7825	7832	7839	7846	1	1	2	3	4	4	5	6	6
1	7853	7860	7868	7875	7882	7889	7896	7903	7910	7917	1	1	2	3	4	4	5	6	6
2	7924	7931	7938	7945	7952	7959	7966	7973	7980	7987	1	1	2	3	3	4	5	6	6
3	7993	8000	8007	8014	8021	8028	8035	8041	8048	8055	1	1	2	3	3	4	5	5	6
4	8062	8069	8075	8082	8089	8096	8102	8109	8116	8122	1	1	2	3	3	4	5	5	6
5	8129	8136	8142	8149	8156	8162	8169	8176	8182	8189	1	1	2	3	3	4	5	5	6
6	8195	8202	8209	8215	8222	8228	8235	8241	8248	8254	1	1	2	3	3	4	5	5	6
7	8261	8267	8274	8280	8287	8293	8299	8306	8312	8319	1	1	2	3	3	4	5	5	6
8	8325	8331	8338	8344	8351	8357	8363	8370	8376	8382	1	1	2	3	3	4	4	5	6
9	8388	8395	8401	8407	8414	8420	8426	8432	8439	8445	1	1	2	2	3	4	4	5	6
0	8451	8457	8463	8470	8476	8482	8488	8494	8500	8506	1	1	2	2	3	4	4	5	6
1	8513	8519	8525	8531	8537	8543	8549	8555	8561	8567	1	1	2	2	3	4	4	5	5
2	8573	8579	8585	8591	8597	8603	8609	8615	8621	8627	1	1	2	2	3	4	4	5	5
3	8633	8639	8645	8651	8657	8663	8669	8675	8681	8686	1	1	2	2	3	4	4	5	5
4	8692	8698	8704	8710	8716	8722	8727	8733	8739	8745	1	1	2	2	3	4	4	5	5
5	8751	8756	8762	8768	8774	8779	8785	8791	8797	8802	1	1	2	2	3	3	4	5	5
6	8808	8814	8820	8825	8831	8837	8842	8848	8854	8859	1	1	2	2	3	3	4	5	5
7	8865	8871	8876	8882	8887	8893	8899	8904	8910	8915	1	1	2	2	3	3	4	4	5
8	8921	8927	8932	8938	8943	8949	8954	8960	8965	8971	1	1	2	2	3	3	4	4	5
9	8976	8982	8987	8993	8998	9004	9009	9015	9020	9025	1	1	2	2	3	3	4	4	5
0	9031	9036	9042	9047	9053	9058	9063	9069	9074	9079	1	1	2	2	3	3	4	4	5
1	9085	9090	9096	9101	9106	9112	9117	9122	9128	9133	1	1	2	2	3	3	4	4	5
2	9138	9143	9149	9154	9159	9165	9170	9175	9180	9186	1	1	2	2	3	3	4	4	5
3	9191	9196	9201	9206	9212	9217	9222	9227	9232	9238	1	1	2	2	3	3	4	4	5
4	9243	9248	9253	9258	9263	9269	9274	9279	9284	9289	1	1	2	2	3	3	4	4	5
5	9294	9299	9304	9309	9315	9320	9325	9330	9335	9340	1	1	2	2	3	3	4	4	5
6	9345	9350	9355	9360	9365	9370	9375	9380	9385	9390	1	1	2	2	3	3	4	4	5
7	9395	9400	9405	9410	9415	9420	9425	9430	9435	9440	0	1	1	2	2	3	3	4	4
8	9445	9450	9455	9460	9465	9469	9474	9479	9484	9489	0	1	1	2	2	3	3	4	4
9	9494	9499	9504	9509	9513	9518	9523	9528	9533	9538	0	1	1	2	2	3	3	4	4
0	9542	9547	9552	9557	9562	9566	9571	9576	9581	9586	0	1	1	2	2	3	3	4	4
1	9590	9595	9600	9605	9609	9614	9619	9624	9628	9633	0	1	1	2	2	3	3	4	4
2	9638	9643	9647	9652	9657	9661	9666	9671	9675	9680	0	1	1	2	2	3	3	4	4
3	9685	9689	9694	9699	9703	9708	9713	9717	9722	9727	0	1	1	2	2	3	3	4	4
4	9731	9736	9741	9745	9750	9754	9759	9763	9768	9773	0	1	1	2	2	3	3	4	4
5	9777	9782	9786	9791	9795	9800	9805	9809	9814	9818	0	1	1	2	2	3	3	4	4
6	9823	9827	9832	9836	9841	9845	9850	9854	9859	9863	0	1	1	2	2	3	3	4	4
7	9868	9872	9877	9881	9886	9890	9894	9899	9903	9908	0	1	1	2	2	3	3	4	4
8	9912	9917	9921	9926	9930	9934	9939	9943	9948	9952	0	1	1	2	2	3	3	4	4
9	9956	9961	9965	9969	9974	9978	9983	9987	9991	9996	0	1	1	2	2	3	3	3	4
	0	1	2	3	4	5	6	7	8	9	1	2	3	4	5	6	7	8	9

10-2

	0	1	2	3	4	5	6	7	8	9	Differences							
											1	2	3	4	5	6	7	8
·00	1000	1002	1005	1007	1009	1012	1014	1016	1019	1021	0	0	1	1	1	1	2	2
·01	1023	1026	1028	1030	1033	1035	1038	1040	1042	1045	0	0	1	1	1	1	2	2
·02	1047	1050	1052	1054	1057	1059	1062	1064	1067	1069	0	0	1	1	1	1	2	2
·03	1072	1074	1076	1079	1081	1084	1086	1089	1091	1094	0	0	1	1	1	1	2	2
·04	1096	1099	1102	1104	1107	1109	1112	1114	1117	1119	0	1	1	1	1	2	2	2
·05	1122	1125	1127	1130	1132	1135	1138	1140	1143	1146	0	1	1	1	1	2	2	2
·06	1148	1151	1153	1156	1159	1161	1164	1167	1169	1172	0	1	1	1	1	2	2	2
·07	1175	1178	1180	1183	1186	1189	1191	1194	1197	1199	0	1	1	1	1	2	2	2
·08	1202	1205	1208	1211	1213	1216	1219	1222	1225	1227	0	1	1	1	1	2	2	2
·09	1230	1233	1236	1239	1242	1245	1247	1250	1253	1256	0	1	1	1	1	2	2	2
·10	1259	1262	1265	1268	1271	1274	1276	1279	1282	1285	0	1	1	1	1	2	2	2
·11	1288	1291	1294	1297	1300	1303	1306	1309	1312	1315	0	1	1	1	2	2	2	2
·12	1318	1321	1324	1327	1330	1334	1337	1340	1343	1346	0	1	1	1	2	2	2	2
·13	1349	1352	1355	1358	1361	1365	1368	1371	1374	1377	0	1	1	1	2	2	2	3
·14	1380	1384	1387	1390	1393	1396	1400	1403	1406	1409	0	1	1	1	2	2	2	3
·15	1413	1416	1419	1422	1426	1429	1432	1435	1439	1442	0	1	1	1	2	2	2	3
·16	1445	1449	1452	1455	1459	1462	1466	1469	1472	1476	0	1	1	1	2	2	2	3
·17	1479	1483	1486	1489	1493	1496	1500	1503	1507	1510	0	1	1	1	2	2	2	3
·18	1514	1517	1521	1524	1528	1531	1535	1538	1542	1545	0	1	1	1	2	2	2	3
·19	1549	1552	1556	1560	1563	1567	1570	1574	1578	1581	0	1	1	1	2	2	3	3
·20	1585	1589	1592	1596	1600	1603	1607	1611	1614	1618	0	1	1	1	2	2	3	3
·21	1622	1626	1629	1633	1637	1641	1644	1648	1652	1656	0	1	1	2	2	2	3	3
·22	1660	1663	1667	1671	1675	1679	1683	1687	1690	1694	0	1	1	2	2	2	3	3
·23	1698	1702	1706	1710	1714	1718	1722	1726	1730	1734	0	1	1	2	2	2	3	3
·24	1738	1742	1746	1750	1754	1758	1762	1766	1770	1774	0	1	1	2	2	2	3	3
·25	1778	1782	1786	1791	1795	1799	1803	1807	1811	1816	0	1	1	2	2	2	3	3
·26	1820	1824	1828	1832	1837	1841	1845	1849	1854	1858	0	1	1	2	2	3	3	3
·27	1862	1866	1871	1875	1879	1884	1888	1892	1897	1901	0	1	1	2	2	3	3	3
·28	1905	1910	1914	1919	1923	1928	1932	1936	1941	1945	0	1	1	2	2	3	3	4
·29	1950	1954	1959	1963	1968	1972	1977	1982	1986	1991	0	1	1	2	2	3	3	4
·30	1995	2000	2004	2009	2014	2018	2023	2028	2032	2037	0	1	1	2	2	3	3	4
·31	2042	2046	2051	2056	2061	2065	2070	2075	2080	2084	0	1	1	2	2	3	3	4
·32	2089	2094	2099	2104	2109	2113	2118	2123	2128	2133	0	1	1	2	2	3	3	4
·33	2138	2143	2148	2153	2158	2163	2168	2173	2178	2183	0	1	1	2	2	3	3	4
·34	2188	2193	2198	2203	2208	2213	2218	2223	2228	2234	1	1	2	2	3	3	4	4
·35	2239	2244	2249	2254	2259	2265	2270	2275	2280	2286	1	1	2	2	3	3	4	4
·36	2291	2296	2301	2307	2312	2317	2323	2328	2333	2339	1	1	2	2	3	3	4	4
·37	2344	2350	2355	2360	2366	2371	2377	2382	2388	2393	1	1	2	2	3	3	4	4
·38	2399	2404	2410	2415	2421	2427	2432	2438	2443	2449	1	1	2	2	3	3	4	4
·39	2455	2460	2466	2472	2477	2483	2489	2495	2500	2506	1	1	2	2	3	3	4	5
·40	2512	2518	2523	2529	2535	2541	2547	2553	2559	2564	1	1	2	2	3	4	4	5
·41	2570	2576	2582	2588	2594	2600	2606	2612	2618	2624	1	1	2	2	3	4	4	5
·42	2630	2636	2642	2649	2655	2661	2667	2673	2679	2685	1	1	2	2	3	4	4	5
·43	2692	2698	2704	2710	2716	2723	2729	2735	2742	2748	1	1	2	3	3	4	4	5
·44	2754	2761	2767	2773	2780	2786	2793	2799	2805	2812	1	1	2	3	3	4	4	5
·45	2818	2825	2831	2838	2844	2851	2858	2864	2871	2877	1	1	2	3	3	4	5	5
·46	2884	2891	2897	2904	2911	2917	2924	2931	2938	2944	1	1	2	3	3	4	5	5
·47	2951	2958	2965	2972	2979	2985	2992	2999	3006	3013	1	1	2	3	3	4	5	5
·48	3020	3027	3034	3041	3048	3055	3062	3069	3076	3083	1	1	2	3	4	4	5	6
·49	3090	3097	3105	3112	3119	3126	3133	3141	3148	3155	1	1	2	3	4	4	5	6
	0	1	2	3	4	5	6	7	8	9	1	2	3	4	5	6	7	8

	0	1	2	3	4	5	6	7	8	9	Differences								
											1	2	3	4	5	6	7	8	9
·50	3162	3170	3177	3184	3192	3199	3206	3214	3221	3228	1	1	2	3	4	4	5	6	7
·51	3236	3243	3251	3258	3266	3273	3281	3289	3296	3304	1	2	2	3	4	5	5	6	7
·52	3311	3319	3327	3334	3342	3350	3357	3365	3373	3381	1	2	2	3	4	5	5	6	7
·53	3388	3396	3404	3412	3420	3428	3436	3443	3451	3459	1	2	2	3	4	5	6	6	7
·54	3467	3475	3483	3491	3499	3508	3516	3524	3532	3540	1	2	2	3	4	5	6	6	7
·55	3548	3556	3565	3573	3581	3589	3597	3606	3614	3622	1	2	2	3	4	5	6	7	7
·56	3631	3639	3648	3656	3664	3673	3681	3690	3698	3707	1	2	3	3	4	5	6	7	8
·57	3715	3724	3733	3741	3750	3758	3767	3776	3784	3793	1	2	3	3	4	5	6	7	8
·58	3802	3811	3819	3828	3837	3846	3855	3864	3873	3882	1	2	3	4	4	5	6	7	8
·59	3890	3899	3908	3917	3926	3936	3945	3954	3963	3972	1	2	3	4	5	5	6	7	8
·60	3981	3990	3999	4009	4018	4027	4036	4046	4055	4064	1	2	3	4	5	6	6	7	8
·61	4074	4083	4093	4102	4111	4121	4130	4140	4150	4159	1	2	3	4	5	6	7	8	9
·62	4169	4178	4188	4198	4207	4217	4227	4236	4246	4256	1	2	3	4	5	6	7	8	9
·63	4266	4276	4285	4295	4305	4315	4325	4335	4345	4355	1	2	3	4	5	6	7	8	9
·64	4365	4375	4385	4395	4406	4416	4426	4436	4446	4457	1	2	3	4	5	6	7	8	9
·65	4467	4477	4487	4498	4508	4519	4529	4539	4550	4560	1	2	3	4	5	6	7	8	9
·66	4571	4581	4592	4603	4613	4624	4634	4645	4656	4667	1	2	3	4	5	6	7	8	10
·67	4677	4688	4699	4710	4721	4732	4742	4753	4764	4775	1	2	3	4	5	7	8	9	10
·68	4786	4797	4808	4819	4831	4842	4853	4864	4875	4887	1	2	3	4	6	7	8	9	10
·69	4898	4909	4920	4932	4943	4955	4966	4977	4989	5000	1	2	3	5	6	7	8	9	10
·70	5012	5023	5035	5047	5058	5070	5082	5093	5105	5117	1	2	4	5	6	7	8	9	11
·71	5129	5140	5152	5164	5176	5188	5200	5212	5224	5236	1	2	4	5	6	7	8	10	11
·72	5248	5260	5272	5284	5297	5309	5321	5333	5346	5358	1	2	4	5	6	7	9	10	11
·73	5370	5383	5395	5408	5420	5433	5445	5458	5470	5483	1	3	4	5	6	8	9	10	11
·74	5495	5508	5521	5534	5546	5559	5572	5585	5598	5610	1	3	4	5	6	8	9	10	12
·75	5623	5636	5649	5662	5675	5689	5702	5715	5728	5741	1	3	4	5	7	8	9	10	12
·76	5754	5768	5781	5794	5808	5821	5834	5848	5861	5875	1	3	4	5	7	8	9	11	12
·77	5888	5902	5916	5929	5943	5957	5970	5984	5998	6012	1	3	4	5	7	8	10	11	12
·78	6026	6039	6053	6067	6081	6095	6109	6124	6138	6152	1	3	4	6	7	8	10	11	13
·79	6166	6180	6194	6209	6223	6237	6252	6266	6281	6295	1	3	4	6	7	9	10	11	13
·80	6310	6324	6339	6353	6368	6383	6397	6412	6427	6442	1	3	4	6	7	9	10	12	13
·81	6457	6471	6486	6501	6516	6531	6546	6561	6577	6592	2	3	5	6	8	9	11	12	14
·82	6607	6622	6637	6653	6668	6683	6699	6714	6730	6745	2	3	5	6	8	9	11	12	14
·83	6761	6776	6792	6808	6823	6839	6855	6871	6887	6902	2	3	5	6	8	9	11	13	14
·84	6918	6934	6950	6966	6982	6998	7015	7031	7047	7063	2	3	5	6	8	10	11	13	15
·85	7079	7096	7112	7129	7145	7161	7178	7194	7211	7228	2	3	5	7	8	10	12	13	15
·86	7244	7261	7278	7295	7311	7328	7345	7362	7379	7396	2	3	5	7	8	10	12	13	15
·87	7413	7430	7447	7464	7482	7499	7516	7534	7551	7568	2	3	5	7	9	10	12	14	16
·88	7586	7603	7621	7638	7656	7674	7691	7709	7727	7745	2	4	5	7	9	11	12	14	16
·89	7762	7780	7798	7816	7834	7852	7870	7889	7907	7925	2	4	5	7	9	11	13	14	16
·90	7943	7962	7980	7998	8017	8035	8054	8072	8091	8110	2	4	6	7	9	11	13	15	17
·91	8128	8147	8166	8185	8204	8222	8241	8260	8279	8299	2	4	6	8	9	11	13	15	17
·92	8318	8337	8356	8375	8395	8414	8433	8453	8472	8492	2	4	6	8	10	12	14	15	17
·93	8511	8531	8551	8570	8590	8610	8630	8650	8670	8690	2	4	6	8	10	12	14	16	18
·94	8710	8730	8750	8770	8790	8810	8831	8851	8872	8892	2	4	6	8	10	12	14	16	18
·95	8913	8933	8954	8974	8995	9016	9036	9057	9078	9099	2	4	6	8	10	12	14	17	19
·96	9120	9141	9162	9183	9204	9226	9247	9268	9290	9311	2	4	6	8	11	13	15	17	19
·97	9333	9354	9376	9397	9419	9441	9462	9484	9506	9528	2	4	7	9	11	13	15	17	20
·98	9550	9572	9594	9616	9638	9661	9683	9705	9727	9750	2	4	7	9	11	13	16	18	20
·99	9772	9795	9817	9840	9863	9886	9908	9931	9954	9977	2	5	7	9	11	14	16	18	20
	0	1	2	3	4	5	6	7	8	9	1	2	3	4	5	6	7	8	9

149

	0	1	2	3	4	5	6	7	8	9	Differences								
											1	2	3	4	5	6	7	8	9
10	1000	1020	1040	1061	1082	1103	1124	1145	1166	1188	2	4	6	8	10	13	15	17	19
11	1210	1232	1254	1277	1300	1323	1346	1369	1392	1416	2	5	7	9	11	14	16	18	21
12	1440	1464	1488	1513	1538	1563	1588	1613	1638	1664	2	5	7	10	12	15	17	20	22
13	1690	1716	1742	1769	1796	1823	1850	1877	1904	1932	3	5	8	11	13	16	19	22	24
14	1960	1988	2016	2045	2074	2103	2132	2161	2190	2220	3	6	9	12	14	17	20	23	26
15	2250	2280	2310	2341	2372	2403	2434	2465	2496	2528	3	6	9	12	15	19	22	25	28
16	2560	2592	2624	2657	2690	2723	2756	2789	2822	2856	3	7	10	13	16	20	23	26	30
17	2890	2924	2958	2993	3028	3063	3098	3133	3168	3204	3	7	10	14	17	21	24	28	31
18	3240	3276	3312	3349	3386	3423	3460	3497	3534	3572	4	7	11	15	18	22	26	30	33
19	3610	3648	3686	3725	3764	3803	3842	3881	3920	3960	4	8	12	16	19	23	27	31	35
20	4000	4040	4080	4121	4162	4203	4244	4285	4326	4368	4	8	12	16	20	25	29	33	37
21	4410	4452	4494	4537	4580	4623	4666	4709	4752	4796	4	9	13	17	21	26	30	34	39
22	4840	4884	4928	4973	5018	5063	5108	5153	5198	5244	4	9	13	18	22	27	31	36	40
23	5290	5336	5382	5429	5476	5523	5570	5617	5664	5712	5	9	14	19	23	28	33	38	42
24	5760	5808	5856	5905	5954	6003	6052	6101	6150	6200	5	10	15	20	24	29	34	39	44
25	6250	6300	6350	6401	6452	6503	6554	6605	6656	6708	5	10	15	20	25	31	36	41	46
26	6760	6812	6864	6917	6970	7023	7076	7129	7182	7236	5	11	16	21	26	32	37	42	48
27	7290	7344	7398	7453	7508	7563	7618	7673	7728	7784	5	11	16	22	27	33	38	44	49
28	7840	7896	7952	8009	8066	8123	8180	8237	8294	8352	6	11	17	23	28	34	40	46	51
29	8410	8468	8526	8585	8644	8703	8762	8821	8880	8940	6	12	18	24	29	35	41	47	53
30	9000	9060	9120	9181	9242	9303	9364	9425	9486	9548	6	12	18	24	30	37	43	49	55
31	9610	9672	9734	9797	9860	9923	9986	—	—	—	6	13	19	25	31	38	44	50	57
31	—	—	—	—	—	—	—	1005	1011	1018	1	1	2	3	3	4	5	5	6
32	1024	1030	1037	1043	1050	1056	1063	1069	1076	1082	1	1	2	3	3	4	5	5	6
33	1089	1096	1102	1109	1116	1122	1129	1136	1142	1149	1	1	2	3	3	4	5	5	6
34	1156	1163	1170	1176	1183	1190	1197	1204	1211	1218	1	1	2	3	3	4	5	6	6
35	1225	1232	1239	1246	1253	1260	1267	1274	1282	1289	1	1	2	3	4	4	5	6	6
36	1296	1303	1310	1318	1325	1332	1340	1347	1354	1362	1	1	2	3	4	4	5	6	7
37	1369	1376	1384	1391	1399	1406	1414	1421	1429	1436	1	2	2	3	4	5	5	6	7
38	1444	1452	1459	1467	1475	1482	1490	1498	1505	1513	1	2	2	3	4	5	5	6	7
39	1521	1529	1537	1544	1552	1560	1568	1576	1584	1592	1	2	2	3	4	5	6	6	7
40	1600	1608	1616	1624	1632	1640	1648	1656	1665	1673	1	2	2	3	4	5	6	6	7
41	1681	1689	1697	1706	1714	1722	1731	1739	1747	1756	1	2	2	3	4	5	6	7	7
42	1764	1772	1781	1789	1798	1806	1815	1823	1832	1840	1	2	3	3	4	5	6	7	8
43	1849	1858	1866	1875	1884	1892	1901	1910	1918	1927	1	2	3	3	4	5	6	7	8
44	1936	1945	1954	1962	1971	1980	1989	1998	2007	2016	1	2	3	4	5	5	6	7	8
45	2025	2034	2043	2052	2061	2070	2079	2088	2098	2107	1	2	3	4	5	5	6	7	8
46	2116	2125	2134	2144	2153	2162	2172	2181	2190	2200	1	2	3	4	5	6	7	7	8
47	2209	2218	2228	2237	2247	2256	2266	2275	2285	2294	1	2	3	4	5	6	7	8	9
48	2304	2314	2323	2333	2343	2352	2362	2372	2381	2391	1	2	3	4	5	6	7	8	9
49	2401	2411	2421	2430	2440	2450	2460	2470	2480	2490	1	2	3	4	5	6	7	8	9
50	2500	2510	2520	2530	2540	2550	2560	2570	2581	2591	1	2	3	4	5	6	7	8	9
51	2601	2611	2621	2632	2642	2652	2663	2673	2683	2694	1	2	3	4	5	6	7	8	9
52	2704	2714	2725	2735	2746	2756	2767	2777	2788	2798	1	2	3	4	5	6	7	8	9
53	2809	2820	2830	2841	2852	2862	2873	2884	2894	2905	1	2	3	4	5	6	7	9	10
54	2916	2927	2938	2948	2959	2970	2981	2992	3003	3014	1	2	3	4	5	7	8	9	10

	0	1	2	3	4	5	6	7	8	9	Differences								
											1	2	3	4	5	6	7	8	9
55	3025	3036	3047	3058	3069	3080	3091	3102	3114	3125	1	2	3	4	6	7	8	9	10
56	3136	3147	3158	3170	3181	3192	3204	3215	3226	3238	1	2	3	5	6	7	8	9	10
57	3249	3260	3272	3283	3295	3306	3318	3329	3341	3352	1	2	3	5	6	7	8	9	10
58	3364	3376	3387	3399	3411	3422	3434	3446	3457	3469	1	2	4	5	6	7	8	9	11
59	3481	3493	3505	3516	3528	3540	3552	3564	3576	3588	1	2	4	5	6	7	8	10	11
60	3600	3612	3624	3636	3648	3660	3672	3684	3697	3709	1	2	4	5	6	7	8	10	11
61	3721	3733	3745	3758	3770	3782	3795	3807	3819	3832	1	2	4	5	6	7	9	10	11
62	3844	3856	3869	3881	3894	3906	3919	3931	3944	3956	1	2	4	5	6	7	9	10	11
63	3969	3982	3994	4007	4020	4032	4045	4058	4070	4083	1	3	4	5	6	8	9	10	11
64	4096	4109	4122	4134	4147	4160	4173	4186	4199	4212	1	3	4	5	6	8	9	10	12
65	4225	4238	4251	4264	4277	4290	4303	4316	4330	4343	1	3	4	5	7	8	9	10	12
66	4356	4369	4382	4396	4409	4422	4436	4449	4462	4476	1	3	4	5	7	8	9	11	12
67	4489	4502	4516	4529	4543	4556	4570	4583	4597	4610	1	3	4	5	7	8	9	11	12
68	4624	4638	4651	4665	4679	4692	4706	4720	4733	4747	1	3	4	5	7	8	10	11	12
69	4761	4775	4789	4802	4816	4830	4844	4858	4872	4886	1	3	4	6	7	8	10	11	13
70	4900	4914	4928	4942	4956	4970	4984	4998	5013	5027	1	3	4	6	7	8	10	11	13
71	5041	5055	5069	5084	5098	5112	5127	5141	5155	5170	1	3	4	6	7	9	10	11	13
72	5184	5198	5213	5227	5242	5256	5271	5285	5300	5314	1	3	4	6	7	9	10	11	13
73	5329	5344	5358	5373	5388	5402	5417	5432	5446	5461	1	3	4	6	7	9	10	12	13
74	5476	5491	5506	5520	5535	5550	5565	5580	5595	5610	1	3	4	6	7	9	10	12	13
75	5625	5640	5655	5670	5685	5700	5715	5730	5746	5761	2	3	5	6	8	9	11	12	14
76	5776	5791	5806	5822	5837	5852	5868	5883	5898	5914	2	3	5	6	8	9	11	12	14
77	5929	5944	5960	5975	5991	6006	6022	6037	6053	6068	2	3	5	6	8	9	11	12	14
78	6084	6100	6115	6131	6147	6162	6178	6194	6209	6225	2	3	5	6	8	9	11	13	14
79	6241	6257	6273	6288	6304	6320	6336	6352	6368	6384	2	3	5	6	8	10	11	13	14
80	6400	6416	6432	6448	6464	6480	6496	6512	6529	6545	2	3	5	6	8	10	11	13	14
81	6561	6577	6593	6610	6626	6642	6659	6675	6691	6708	2	3	5	7	8	10	11	13	15
82	6724	6740	6757	6773	6790	6806	6823	6839	6856	6872	2	3	5	7	8	10	12	13	15
83	6889	6906	6922	6939	6956	6972	6989	7006	7022	7039	2	3	5	7	8	10	12	13	15
84	7056	7073	7090	7106	7123	7140	7157	7174	7191	7208	2	3	5	7	8	10	12	14	15
85	7225	7242	7259	7276	7293	7310	7327	7344	7362	7379	2	3	5	7	9	10	12	14	15
86	7396	7413	7430	7448	7465	7482	7500	7517	7534	7552	2	3	5	7	9	10	12	14	16
87	7569	7586	7604	7621	7639	7656	7674	7691	7709	7726	2	3	5	7	9	10	12	14	16
88	7744	7762	7779	7797	7815	7832	7850	7868	7885	7903	2	4	5	7	9	11	12	14	16
89	7921	7939	7957	7974	7992	8010	8028	8046	8064	8082	2	4	5	7	9	11	13	14	16
90	8100	8118	8136	8154	8172	8190	8208	8226	8245	8263	2	4	5	7	9	11	13	14	16
91	8281	8299	8317	8336	8354	8372	8391	8409	8427	8446	2	4	5	7	9	11	13	15	16
92	8464	8482	8501	8519	8538	8556	8575	8593	8612	8630	2	4	6	7	9	11	13	15	17
93	8649	8668	8686	8705	8724	8742	8761	8780	8798	8817	2	4	6	7	9	11	13	15	17
94	8836	8855	8874	8892	8911	8930	8949	8968	8987	9006	2	4	6	8	9	11	13	15	17
95	9025	9044	9063	9082	9101	9120	9139	9158	9178	9197	2	4	6	8	10	11	13	15	17
96	9216	9235	9254	9274	9293	9312	9332	9351	9370	9390	2	4	6	8	10	12	14	15	17
97	9409	9428	9448	9467	9487	9506	9526	9545	9565	9584	2	4	6	8	10	12	14	16	18
98	9604	9624	9643	9663	9683	9702	9722	9742	9761	9781	2	4	6	8	10	12	14	16	18
99	9801	9821	9841	9860	9880	9900	9920	9940	9960	9980	2	4	6	8	10	12	14	16	18

	0	1	2	3	4	5	6	7	8	9	Differences 1 2 3	4 5 6	7 8 9
1·0	1·000	1·005	1·010	1·015	1·020	1·025	1·030	1·034	1·039	1·044	0 1 1	2 2 3	3 4 4
1·1	1·049	1·054	1·058	1·063	1·068	1·072	1·077	1·082	1·086	1·091	0 1 1	2 2 3	3 4 4
1·2	1·095	1·100	1·105	1·109	1·114	1·118	1·122	1·127	1·131	1·136	0 1 1	2 2 3	3 4 4
1·3	1·140	1·145	1·149	1·153	1·158	1·162	1·166	1·170	1·175	1·179	0 1 1	2 2 3	3 3 4
1·4	1·183	1·187	1·192	1·196	1·200	1·204	1·208	1·212	1·217	1·221	0 1 1	2 2 2	3 3 4
1·5	1·225	1·229	1·233	1·237	1·241	1·245	1·249	1·253	1·257	1·261	0 1 1	2 2 2	3 3 4
1·6	1·265	1·269	1·273	1·277	1·281	1·285	1·288	1·292	1·296	1·300	0 1 1	2 2 2	3 3 4
1·7	1·304	1·308	1·311	1·315	1·319	1·323	1·327	1·330	1·334	1·338	0 1 1	2 2 2	3 3 3
1·8	1·342	1·345	1·349	1·353	1·356	1·360	1·364	1·367	1·371	1·375	0 1 1	1 2 2	3 3 3
1·9	1·378	1·382	1·386	1·389	1·393	1·396	1·400	1·404	1·407	1·411	0 1 1	1 2 2	3 3 3
2·0	1·414	1·418	1·421	1·425	1·428	1·432	1·435	1·439	1·442	1·446	0 1 1	1 2 2	2 3 3
2·1	1·449	1·453	1·456	1·459	1·463	1·466	1·470	1·473	1·476	1·480	0 1 1	1 2 2	2 3 3
2·2	1·483	1·487	1·490	1·493	1·497	1·500	1·503	1·507	1·510	1·513	0 1 1	1 2 2	2 3 3
2·3	1·517	1·520	1·523	1·526	1·530	1·533	1·536	1·539	1·543	1·546	0 1 1	1 2 2	2 3 3
2·4	1·549	1·552	1·556	1·559	1·562	1·565	1·568	1·572	1·575	1·578	0 1 1	1 2 2	2 3 3
2·5	1·581	1·584	1·587	1·591	1·594	1·597	1·600	1·603	1·606	1·609	0 1 1	1 2 2	2 3 3
2·6	1·612	1·616	1·619	1·622	1·625	1·628	1·631	1·634	1·637	1·640	0 1 1	1 2 2	2 2 3
2·7	1·643	1·646	1·649	1·652	1·655	1·658	1·661	1·664	1·667	1·670	0 1 1	1 2 2	2 2 3
2·8	1·673	1·676	1·679	1·682	1·685	1·688	1·691	1·694	1·697	1·700	0 1 1	1 1 2	2 2 3
2·9	1·703	1·706	1·709	1·712	1·715	1·718	1·720	1·723	1·726	1·729	0 1 1	1 1 2	2 2 3
3·0	1·732	1·735	1·738	1·741	1·744	1·746	1·749	1·752	1·755	1·758	0 1 1	1 1 2	2 2 3
3·1	1·761	1·764	1·766	1·769	1·772	1·775	1·778	1·780	1·783	1·786	0 1 1	1 1 2	2 2 3
3·2	1·789	1·792	1·794	1·797	1·800	1·803	1·806	1·808	1·811	1·814	0 1 1	1 1 2	2 2 2
3·3	1·817	1·819	1·822	1·825	1·828	1·830	1·833	1·836	1·838	1·841	0 1 1	1 1 2	2 2 2
3·4	1·844	1·847	1·849	1·852	1·855	1·857	1·860	1·863	1·865	1·868	0 1 1	1 1 2	2 2 2
3·5	1·871	1·873	1·876	1·879	1·881	1·884	1·887	1·889	1·892	1·895	0 1 1	1 1 2	2 2 2
3·6	1·897	1·900	1·903	1·905	1·908	1·910	1·913	1·916	1·918	1·921	0 1 1	1 1 2	2 2 2
3·7	1·924	1·926	1·929	1·931	1·934	1·936	1·939	1·942	1·944	1·947	0 1 1	1 1 2	2 2 2
3·8	1·949	1·952	1·954	1·957	1·960	1·962	1·965	1·967	1·970	1·972	0 1 1	1 1 2	2 2 2
3·9	1·975	1·977	1·980	1·982	1·985	1·987	1·990	1·992	1·995	1·997	0 1 1	1 1 2	2 2 2
4·0	2·000	2·002	2·005	2·007	2·010	2·012	2·015	2·017	2·020	2·022	0 0 1	1 1 1	2 2 2
4·1	2·025	2·027	2·030	2·032	2·035	2·037	2·040	2·042	2·045	2·047	0 0 1	1 1 1	2 2 2
4·2	2·049	2·052	2·054	2·057	2·059	2·062	2·064	2·066	2·069	2·071	0 0 1	1 1 1	2 2 2
4·3	2·074	2·076	2·078	2·081	2·083	2·086	2·088	2·090	2·093	2·095	0 0 1	1 1 1	2 2 2
4·4	2·098	2·100	2·102	2·105	2·107	2·110	2·112	2·114	2·117	2·119	0 0 1	1 1 1	2 2 2
4·5	2·121	2·124	2·126	2·128	2·131	2·133	2·135	2·138	2·140	2·142	0 0 1	1 1 1	2 2 2
4·6	2·145	2·147	2·149	2·152	2·154	2·156	2·159	2·161	2·163	2·166	0 0 1	1 1 1	2 2 2
4·7	2·168	2·170	2·173	2·175	2·177	2·179	2·182	2·184	2·186	2·189	0 0 1	1 1 1	2 2 2
4·8	2·191	2·193	2·195	2·198	2·200	2·202	2·205	2·207	2·209	2·211	0 0 1	1 1 1	2 2 2
4·9	2·214	2·216	2·218	2·220	2·223	2·225	2·227	2·229	2·232	2·234	0 0 1	1 1 1	2 2 2
5·0	2·236	2·238	2·241	2·243	2·245	2·247	2·249	2·252	2·254	2·256	0 0 1	1 1 1	2 2 2
5·1	2·258	2·261	2·263	2·265	2·267	2·269	2·272	2·274	2·276	2·278	0 0 1	1 1 1	2 2 2
5·2	2·280	2·283	2·285	2·287	2·289	2·291	2·293	2·296	2·298	2·300	0 0 1	1 1 1	2 2 2
5·3	2·302	2·304	2·307	2·309	2·311	2·313	2·315	2·317	2·319	2·322	0 0 1	1 1 1	2 2 2
5·4	2·324	2·326	2·328	2·330	2·332	2·335	2·337	2·339	2·341	2·343	0 0 1	1 1 1	1 2 2

	0	1	2	3	4	5	6	7	8	9	Differences								
											1	2	3	4	5	6	7	8	9
5·5	2·345	2·347	2·349	2·352	2·354	2·356	2·358	2·360	2·362	2·364	0	0	1	1	1	1	1	2	2
5·6	2·366	2·369	2·371	2·373	2·375	2·377	2·379	2·381	2·383	2·385	0	0	1	1	1	1	1	2	2
5·7	2·387	2·390	2·392	2·394	2·396	2·398	2·400	2·402	2·404	2·406	0	0	1	1	1	1	1	2	2
5·8	2·408	2·410	2·412	2·415	2·417	2·419	2·421	2·423	2·425	2·427	0	0	1	1	1	1	1	2	2
5·9	2·429	2·431	2·433	2·435	2·437	2·439	2·441	2·443	2·445	2·447	0	0	1	1	1	1	1	2	2
6·0	2·449	2·452	2·454	2·456	2·458	2·460	2·462	2·464	2·466	2·468	0	0	1	1	1	1	1	2	2
6·1	2·470	2·472	2·474	2·476	2·478	2·480	2·482	2·484	2·486	2·488	0	0	1	1	1	1	1	2	2
6·2	2·490	2·492	2·494	2·496	2·498	2·500	2·502	2·504	2·506	2·508	0	0	1	1	1	1	1	2	2
6·3	2·510	2·512	2·514	2·516	2·518	2·520	2·522	2·524	2·526	2·528	0	0	1	1	1	1	1	2	2
6·4	2·530	2·532	2·534	2·536	2·538	2·540	2·542	2·544	2·546	2·548	0	0	1	1	1	1	1	2	2
6·5	2·550	2·551	2·553	2·555	2·557	2·559	2·561	2·563	2·565	2·567	0	0	1	1	1	1	1	2	2
6·6	2·569	2·571	2·573	2·575	2·577	2·579	2·581	2·583	2·585	2·587	0	0	1	1	1	1	1	2	2
6·7	2·588	2·590	2·592	2·594	2·596	2·598	2·600	2·602	2·604	2·606	0	0	1	1	1	1	1	2	2
6·8	2·608	2·610	2·612	2·613	2·615	2·617	2·619	2·621	2·623	2·625	0	0	1	1	1	1	1	2	2
6·9	2·627	2·629	2·631	2·632	2·634	2·636	2·638	2·640	2·642	2·644	0	0	1	1	1	1	1	2	2
7·0	2·646	2·648	2·650	2·651	2·653	2·655	2·657	2·659	2·661	2·663	0	0	1	1	1	1	1	2	2
7·1	2·665	2·666	2·668	2·670	2·672	2·674	2·676	2·678	2·680	2·681	0	0	1	1	1	1	1	1	2
7·2	2·683	2·685	2·687	2·689	2·691	2·693	2·694	2·696	2·698	2·700	0	0	1	1	1	1	1	1	2
7·3	2·702	2·704	2·706	2·707	2·709	2·711	2·713	2·715	2·717	2·718	0	0	1	1	1	1	1	1	2
7·4	2·720	2·722	2·724	2·726	2·728	2·729	2·731	2·733	2·735	2·737	0	0	1	1	1	1	1	1	2
7·5	2·739	2·740	2·742	2·744	2·746	2·748	2·750	2·751	2·753	2·755	0	0	1	1	1	1	1	1	2
7·6	2·757	2·759	2·760	2·762	2·764	2·766	2·768	2·769	2·771	2·773	0	0	1	1	1	1	1	1	2
7·7	2·775	2·777	2·778	2·780	2·782	2·784	2·786	2·787	2·789	2·791	0	0	1	1	1	1	1	1	2
7·8	2·793	2·795	2·796	2·798	2·800	2·802	2·804	2·805	2·807	2·809	0	0	1	1	1	1	1	1	2
7·9	2·811	2·812	2·814	2·816	2·818	2·820	2·821	2·823	2·825	2·827	0	0	1	1	1	1	1	1	2
8·0	2·828	2·830	2·832	2·834	2·835	2·837	2·839	2·841	2·843	2·844	0	0	1	1	1	1	1	1	2
8·1	2·846	2·848	2·850	2·851	2·853	2·855	2·857	2·858	2·860	2·862	0	0	1	1	1	1	1	1	2
8·2	2·864	2·865	2·867	2·869	2·871	2·872	2·874	2·876	2·877	2·879	0	0	1	1	1	1	1	1	2
8·3	2·881	2·883	2·884	2·886	2·888	2·890	2·891	2·893	2·895	2·897	0	0	1	1	1	1	1	1	2
8·4	2·898	2·900	2·902	2·903	2·905	2·907	2·909	2·910	2·912	2·914	0	0	1	1	1	1	1	1	2
8·5	2·915	2·917	2·919	2·921	2·922	2·924	2·926	2·927	2·929	2·931	0	0	1	1	1	1	1	1	2
8·6	2·933	2·934	2·936	2·938	2·939	2·941	2·943	2·944	2·946	2·948	0	0	1	1	1	1	1	1	2
8·7	2·950	2·951	2·953	2·955	2·956	2·958	2·960	2·961	2·963	2·965	0	0	1	1	1	1	1	1	2
8·8	2·966	2·968	2·970	2·972	2·973	2·975	2·977	2·978	2·980	2·982	0	0	1	1	1	1	1	1	2
8·9	2·983	2·985	2·987	2·988	2·990	2·992	2·993	2·995	2·997	2·998	0	0	1	1	1	1	1	1	2
9·0	3·000	3·002	3·003	3·005	3·007	3·008	3·010	3·012	3·013	3·015	0	0	0	1	1	1	1	1	1
9·1	3·017	3·018	3·020	3·022	3·023	3·025	3·027	3·028	3·030	3·032	0	0	0	1	1	1	1	1	1
9·2	3·033	3·035	3·036	3·038	3·040	3·041	3·043	3·045	3·046	3·048	0	0	0	1	1	1	1	1	1
9·3	3·050	3·051	3·053	3·055	3·056	3·058	3·059	3·061	3·063	3·064	0	0	0	1	1	1	1	1	1
9·4	3·066	3·068	3·069	3·071	3·072	3·074	3·076	3·077	3·079	3·081	0	0	0	1	1	1	1	1	1
9·5	3·082	3·084	3·085	3·087	3·089	3·090	3·092	3·094	3·095	3·097	0	0	0	1	1	1	1	1	1
9·6	3·098	3·100	3·102	3·103	3·105	3·106	3·108	3·110	3·111	3·113	0	0	0	1	1	1	1	1	1
9·7	3·114	3·116	3·118	3·119	3·121	3·122	3·124	3·126	3·127	3·129	0	0	0	1	1	1	1	1	1
9·8	3·130	3·132	3·134	3·135	3·137	3·138	3·140	3·142	3·143	3·145	0	0	0	1	1	1	1	1	1
9·9	3·146	3·148	3·150	3·151	3·153	3·154	3·156	3·158	3·159	3·161	0	0	0	1	1	1	1	1	1

	0	1	2	3	4	5	6	7	8	9	Differences 1	2	3	4	5	6	7	8	9
10	3·162	3·178	3·194	3·209	3·225	3·240	3·256	3·271	3·286	3·302	2	3	5	6	8	9	11	12	1
11	3·317	3·332	3·347	3·362	3·376	3·391	3·406	3·421	3·435	3·450	1	3	4	6	7	9	10	12	1
12	3·464	3·479	3·493	3·507	3·521	3·536	3·550	3·564	3·578	3·592	1	3	4	6	7	8	10	11	1
13	3·606	3·619	3·633	3·647	3·661	3·674	3·688	3·701	3·715	3·728	1	3	4	5	7	8	10	11	1
14	3·742	3·755	3·768	3·782	3·795	3·808	3·821	3·834	3·847	3·860	1	3	4	5	7	8	9	11	1
15	3·873	3·886	3·899	3·912	3·924	3·937	3·950	3·962	3·975	3·987	1	3	4	5	6	8	9	10	1
16	4·000	4·012	4·025	4·037	4·050	4·062	4·074	4·087	4·099	4·111	1	2	4	5	6	7	9	10	1
17	4·123	4·135	4·147	4·159	4·171	4·183	4·195	4·207	4·219	4·231	1	2	4	5	6	7	8	10	1
18	4·243	4·254	4·266	4·278	4·290	4·30ı	4·313	4·324	4·336	4·347	1	2	3	5	6	7	8	9	1
19	4·359	4·370	4·382	4·393	4·405	4·416	4·427	4·438	4·450	4·461	1	2	3	5	6	7	8	9	1
20	4·472	4·483	4·494	4·506	4·517	4·528	4·539	4·550	4·561	4·572	1	2	3	4	6	7	8	9	1
21	4·583	4·593	4·604	4·615	4·626	4·637	4·648	4·658	4·669	4·680	1	2	3	4	5	6	8	9	1
22	4·690	4·701	4·712	4·722	4·733	4·743	4·754	4·764	4·775	4·785	1	2	3	4	5	6	7	8	
23	4·796	4·806	4·817	4·827	4·837	4·848	4·858	4·868	4·879	4·889	1	2	3	4	5	6	7	8	
24	4·899	4·909	4·919	4·930	4·940	4·950	4·960	4·970	4·980	4·990	1	2	3	4	5	6	7	8	
25	5·000	5·010	5·020	5·030	5·040	5·050	5·060	5·070	5·079	5·089	1	2	3	4	5	6	7	8	
26	5·099	5·109	5·119	5·128	5·138	5·148	5·158	5·167	5·177	5·187	1	2	3	4	5	6	7	8	
27	5·196	5·206	5·215	5·225	5·235	5·244	5·254	5·263	5·273	5·282	1	2	3	4	5	6	7	8	
28	5·292	5·301	5·310	5·320	5·329	5·339	5·348	5·357	5·367	5·376	1	2	3	4	5	6	7	7	
29	5·385	5·394	5·404	5·413	5·422	5·431	5·441	5·450	5·459	5·468	1	2	3	4	5	5	6	7	
30	5·477	5·486	5·495	5·505	5·514	5·523	5·532	5·541	5·550	5·559	1	2	3	4	4	5	6	7	
31	5·568	5·577	5·586	5·595	5·604	5·612	5·621	5·630	5·639	5·648	1	2	3	3	4	5	6	7	
32	5·657	5·666	5·675	5·683	5·692	5·701	5·710	5·718	5·727	5·736	1	2	3	3	4	5	6	7	
33	5·745	5·753	5·762	5·771	5·779	5·788	5·797	5·805	5·814	5·822	1	2	3	3	4	5	6	7	
34	5·831	5·840	5·848	5·857	5·865	5·874	5·882	5·891	5·899	5·908	1	2	3	3	4	5	6	7	
35	5·916	5·925	5·933	5·941	5·950	5·958	5·967	5·975	5·983	5·992	1	2	2	3	4	5	6	7	
36	6·000	6·008	6·017	6·025	6·033	6·042	6·050	6·058	6·066	6·075	1	2	2	3	4	5	6	7	
37	6·083	6·091	6·099	6·107	6·116	6·124	6·132	6·140	6·148	6·156	1	2	2	3	4	5	6	7	
38	6·164	6·173	6·181	6·189	6·197	6·205	6·213	6·221	6·229	6·237	1	2	2	3	4	5	6	6	
39	6·245	6·253	6·261	6·269	6·277	6·285	6·293	6·301	6·309	6·317	1	2	2	3	4	5	6	6	
40	6·325	6·332	6·340	6·348	6·356	6·364	6·372	6·380	6·387	6·395	1	2	2	3	4	5	6	6	
41	6·403	6·411	6·419	6·427	6·434	6·442	6·450	6·458	6·465	6·473	1	2	2	3	4	5	5	6	
42	6·481	6·488	6·496	6·504	6·512	6·519	6·527	6·535	6·542	6·550	1	2	2	3	4	5	5	6	
43	6·557	6·565	6·573	6·580	6·588	6·595	6·603	6·611	6·618	6·626	1	2	2	3	4	5	5	6	
44	6·633	6·641	6·648	6·656	6·663	6·671	6·678	6·686	6·693	6·701	1	1	2	3	4	4	5	6	
45	6·708	6·716	6·723	6·731	6·738	6·745	6·753	6·760	6·768	6·775	1	1	2	3	4	4	5	6	
46	6·782	6·790	6·797	6·804	6·812	6·819	6·826	6·834	6·841	6·848	1	1	2	3	4	4	5	6	
47	6·856	6·863	6·870	6·877	6·885	6·892	6·899	6·907	6·914	6·921	1	1	2	3	4	4	5	6	
48	6·928	6·935	6·943	6·950	6·957	6·964	6·971	6·979	6·986	6·993	1	1	2	3	4	4	5	6	
49	7·000	7·007	7·014	7·021	7·029	7·036	7·043	7·050	7·057	7·064	1	1	2	3	4	4	5	6	
50	7·071	7·078	7·085	7·092	7·099	7·106	7·113	7·120	7·127	7·134	1	1	2	3	4	4	5	6	
51	7·141	7·148	7·155	7·162	7·169	7·176	7·183	7·190	7·197	7·204	1	1	2	3	4	4	5	6	
52	7·211	7·218	7·225	7·232	7·239	7·246	7·253	7·259	7·266	7·273	1	1	2	3	3	4	5	6	
53	7·280	7·287	7·294	7·301	7·308	7·314	7·321	7·328	7·335	7·342	1	1	2	3	3	4	5	5	
54	7·348	7·355	7·362	7·369	7·376	7·382	7·389	7·396	7·403	7·409	1	1	2	3	3	4	5	5	

	0	1	2	3	4	5	6	7	8	9	Differences								
											1	2	3	4	5	6	7	8	9
55	7·416	7·423	7·430	7·436	7·443	7·450	7·457	7·463	7·470	7·477	1	1	2	3	3	4	5	5	6
56	7·483	7·490	7·497	7·503	7·510	7·517	7·523	7·530	7·537	7·543	1	1	2	3	3	4	5	5	6
57	7·550	7·556	7·563	7·570	7·576	7·583	7·589	7·596	7·603	7·609	1	1	2	3	3	4	5	5	6
58	7·616	7·622	7·629	7·635	7·642	7·649	7·655	7·662	7·668	7·675	1	1	2	3	3	4	5	5	6
59	7·681	7·688	7·694	7·701	7·707	7·714	7·720	7·727	7·733	7·740	1	1	2	3	3	4	5	5	6
60	7·746	7·752	7·759	7·765	7·772	7·778	7·785	7·791	7·797	7·804	1	1	2	3	3	4	4	5	6
61	7·810	7·817	7·823	7·829	7·836	7·842	7·849	7·855	7·861	7·868	1	1	2	3	3	4	4	5	6
62	7·874	7·880	7·887	7·893	7·899	7·906	7·912	7·918	7·925	7·931	1	1	2	3	3	4	4	5	6
63	7·937	7·944	7·950	7·956	7·962	7·969	7·975	7·981	7·987	7·994	1	1	2	3	3	4	4	5	6
64	8·000	8·006	8·012	8·019	8·025	8·031	8·037	8·044	8·050	8·056	1	1	2	2	3	4	4	5	6
65	8·062	8·068	8·075	8·081	8·087	8·093	8·099	8·106	8·112	8·118	1	1	2	2	3	4	4	5	6
66	8·124	8·130	8·136	8·142	8·149	8·155	8·161	8·167	8·173	8·179	1	1	2	2	3	4	4	5	5
67	8·185	8·191	8·198	8·204	8·210	8·216	8·222	8·228	8·234	8·240	1	1	2	2	3	4	4	5	5
68	8·246	8·252	8·258	8·264	8·270	8·276	8·283	8·289	8·295	8·301	1	1	2	2	3	4	4	5	5
69	8·307	8·313	8·319	8·325	8·331	8·337	8·343	8·349	8·355	8·361	1	1	2	2	3	4	4	5	5
70	8·367	8·373	8·379	8·385	8·390	8·396	8·402	8·408	8·414	8·420	1	1	2	2	3	4	4	5	5
71	8·426	8·432	8·438	8·444	8·450	8·456	8·462	8·468	8·473	8·479	1	1	2	2	3	4	4	5	5
72	8·485	8·491	8·497	8·503	8·509	8·515	8·521	8·526	8·532	8·538	1	1	2	2	3	3	4	5	5
73	8·544	8·550	8·556	8·562	8·567	8·573	8·579	8·585	8·591	8·597	1	1	2	2	3	3	4	5	5
74	8·602	8·608	8·614	8·620	8·626	8·631	8·637	8·643	8·649	8·654	1	1	2	2	3	3	4	5	5
75	8·660	8·666	8·672	8·678	8·683	8·689	8·695	8·701	8·706	8·712	1	1	2	2	3	3	4	5	5
76	8·718	8·724	8·729	8·735	8·741	8·746	8·752	8·758	8·764	8·769	1	1	2	2	3	3	4	5	5
77	8·775	8·781	8·786	8·792	8·798	8·803	8·809	8·815	8·820	8·826	1	1	2	2	3	3	4	4	5
78	8·832	8·837	8·843	8·849	8·854	8·860	8·866	8·871	8·877	8·883	1	1	2	2	3	3	4	4	5
79	8·888	8·894	8·899	8·905	8·911	8·916	8·922	8·927	8·933	8·939	1	1	2	2	3	3	4	4	5
80	8·944	8·950	8·955	8·961	8·967	8·972	8·978	8·983	8·989	8·994	1	1	2	2	3	3	4	4	5
81	9·000	9·006	9·011	9·017	9·022	9·028	9·033	9·039	9·044	9·050	1	1	2	2	3	3	4	4	5
82	9·055	9·061	9·066	9·072	9·077	9·083	9·088	9·094	9·099	9·105	1	1	2	2	3	3	4	4	5
83	9·110	9·116	9·121	9·127	9·132	9·138	9·143	9·149	9·154	9·160	1	1	2	2	3	3	4	4	5
84	9·165	9·171	9·176	9·182	9·187	9·192	9·198	9·203	9·209	9·214	1	1	2	2	3	3	4	4	5
85	9·220	9·225	9·230	9·236	9·241	9·247	9·252	9·257	9·263	9·268	1	1	2	2	3	3	4	4	5
86	9·274	9·279	9·284	9·290	9·295	9·301	9·306	9·311	9·317	9·322	1	1	2	2	3	3	4	4	5
87	9·327	9·333	9·338	9·343	9·349	9·354	9·359	9·365	9·370	9·375	1	1	2	2	3	3	4	4	5
88	9·381	9·386	9·391	9·397	9·402	9·407	9·413	9·418	9·423	9·429	1	1	2	2	3	3	4	4	5
89	9·434	9·439	9·445	9·450	9·455	9·460	9·466	9·471	9·476	9·482	1	1	2	2	3	3	4	4	5
90	9·487	9·492	9·497	9·503	9·508	9·513	9·518	9·524	9·529	9·534	1	1	2	2	3	3	4	4	5
91	9·539	9·545	9·550	9·555	9·560	9·566	9·571	9·576	9·581	9·586	1	1	2	2	3	3	4	4	5
92	9·592	9·597	9·602	9·607	9·612	9·618	9·623	9·628	9·633	9·638	1	1	2	2	3	3	4	4	5
93	9·644	9·649	9·654	9·659	9·664	9·670	9·675	9·680	9·685	9·690	1	1	2	2	3	3	4	4	5
94	9·695	9·701	9·706	9·711	9·716	9·721	9·726	9·731	9·737	9·742	1	1	2	2	3	3	4	4	5
95	9·747	9·752	9·757	9·762	9·767	9·772	9·778	9·783	9·788	9·793	1	1	2	2	3	3	4	4	5
96	9·798	9·803	9·808	9·813	9·818	9·823	9·829	9·834	9·839	9·844	1	1	2	2	3	3	4	4	5
97	9·849	9·854	9·859	9·864	9·869	9·874	9·879	9·884	9·889	9·894	1	1	2	2	3	3	4	4	5
98	9·899	9·905	9·910	9·915	9·920	9·925	9·930	9·935	9·940	9·945	0	1	1	2	2	3	3	4	4
99	9·950	9·955	9·960	9·965	9·970	9·975	9·980	9·985	9·990	9·995	0	1	1	2	2	3	3	4	4